J. S. BACH

THE PASSION ACCORDING TO ST. JOHN

VOCAL SCORE EDITED AND
WITH AN INTRODUCTION BY
ARTHUR MENDEL

Ed. 1967

G. SCHIRMER, *Inc.*

DISTRIBUTED BY

HAL•LEONARD
CORPORATION
7777 W. BLUEMOUND RD. P.O. BOX 13819 MILWAUKEE, WI 53213

TABLE OF CONTENTS

INTRODUCTION

I. Nature, Sources, and Meanings of the Bach-Gesellschaft Text

From the chaste, clear, definitive-looking pages of a Bach-Gesellschaft volume it is easy to get a false impression of a work by Bach. "This", we are in the habit of thinking and telling each other, "is the authentic text—just what Bach wrote, no more, no less". It is true that for some few Bach works such an authentic text can be established, or at least closely approached. They are works which were engraved, published, and even corrected in later printings, all under Bach's own direct supervision. There are others of which, for one reason or another, he prepared a "fair copy" of what he presumably considered the final version.

But even if the St. John Passion were one of these—and it is not—there are two main reasons why the definitiveness of "the authentic text" would remain only relative.

The first is that while we look up to Bach's music as to a sort of Holy Writ, nothing indicates that he himself had any notion that it would ever be particularly famous. His contemporaries considered him an extremely able and learned musician, but nothing that happened during his life-time foreshadowed the canonization that posterity has accorded him. If he had known that all his works would one day be published, studied, and argued over, he might easily have inserted some intentional puzzles to annoy future editors, but he certainly would have provided clear and final texts for many more works than he did.

The second reason is that printed symbols mean different things to different ages, nations, schools of thought, and individuals, so that even a text published and revised under Bach's own eyes was completely clear only to those who knew exactly what each symbol meant to him, as we cannot know with certainty today. It is no use, of course, trying to establish what these symbols "really" mean, but only what Bach meant by them.

* * *

Where did the Bach-Gesellschaft editor get his authentic-looking text for the St. John Passion?

The full account of his sources is translated on pp. 232-241 of this vocal score, so it may be summarized here. The sources consisted of an "original" manuscript score of which only the first ten pages (according to Spitta) are in Bach's handwriting;* another manuscript score in the handwriting of a member of Carl Philipp Emanuel Bach's choir in Hamburg; and many "original" manuscript vocal and instrumental parts, few of them in Bach's handwriting, but almost all containing some markings believed to be autograph.

"Original" in this sense refers to score and parts made and used for performance under Bach's own direction. It does not mean "earliest", for the

---

*These pages are reproduced in facsimile in Jahrg. XLIV of the Bach-Gesellschaft edition. The English translator of Spitta agrees with the BG editor in saying that the original score contains twenty (not ten) autograph pages. Who is in error I cannot say, but Spitta's German text is in general more reliable than either of the other sources.

original parts fall into three groups belonging to three different times, and the original score was made at least as late as the final group of parts (Spitta, who knew most about it, says "after" them).

The pages of the original parts in Bach's handwriting belong mostly to the movements numbered 1, 31, and 32 in this vocal score. None of these three movements were included in the first version of the work. Bach wrote them to replace other movements of which he discarded some and transplanted others. The most conspicuous of these transplantations affected the movement *O Mensch, bewein' dein' Sünde gross*, originally written (in Eb) as the opening movement of the St. John, and later used (in E) to close the first part of the St. Matthew.*

It was Wilhelm Rust, the editor of the BG edition, who first sorted out all of this manuscript material and separated the "original" parts into three groups: "earlier", "middle", and "later". Spitta confirmed most of Rust's conclusions and corrected others. No thorough study of the material has been published since Spitta's day.

The achievements of Rust and Spitta were monumental, and I know of no reason to doubt any of their principal conclusions. They both accepted the "original" score as representing, though not very accurately in detail, Bach's final intentions. But from the many loose ends that are left after all of Rust's efforts to reconcile the various sources, it is clear that the beautifully engraved pages of his edition represent an order imposed (of necessity) partly by him on a rather disorganized mass of material. It does not—no single score could—represent "just what Bach wrote, no more, no less". Rust gives a fairly detailed account of the contradictions contained in the sources, but it is by no means a full account, and it leaves many questions unanswered. To make a single score out of the material, he had to make innumerable editorial choices. Several of these he could mention; most of them we have no way of recognizing as editorial choices, although in a few instances it seems possible to identify them and even guess at what may be in the original material.

This new edition, then, represents mainly a reproduction of the voice parts and a reduction for keyboard instrument of the instrumental parts found in the BG score, which in turn represents a digest—not a complete rendering— of the original source material. This vocal score also represents an attempt to determine what Bach meant by the notation he used, as far as BG and its sources permit us to know what that notation was.

The symbols that have a meaning for us different from what they had for Bach include not only notes, rests, and time-signatures, but words used to describe the character or the tempo of the music as well as its texture and even its performers. When we read in the musical dictionary written by Bach's friend J. G. Walther, and published in Leipzig in 1732, the term *Allegro ed andante*, we realize that either *allegro* or *andante* or both have changed their meanings since Bach's time. When Bach marks the $\frac{3}{4}$ section of *Es ist vollbracht* (No. 58 of this score) "*Alla breve*", or *Mein teurer Heiland* (No. 60) "*Adagio*", and the 'cello obbligato of the same number "*spiccato*", the modern musician is puzzled.

---

*A full account of the other substitutions is given by the BG editor and Spitta, and there is a summary account by Terry in his pamphlet *Bach, the Passions* in the Musical Pilgrim series published by Oxford University Press.

Misunderstandings begin on the very first page. Bach heads the first number "Coro" (chorus) and lists the instruments and voices at the left of the staves representing them in the first system of his score. Of the eleven names for instruments and voices, seven are misleading, in the sense that while they are terms currently in use today, they mean something quite different to us from what they meant to Bach. To avoid such misunderstandings, it will be best to trace briefly the history of this work.

II. History and Structure

When Bach produced the St. John Passion for the first time, on Good Friday, 1723 (or 1724), in Leipzig, he was bringing toward its climax a developing tradition that reached far back into the Middle Ages. It was an ancient church custom to sing the Passion story with one voice chanting the Gospel narrative and one or more other voices representing the protagonists of the drama. The practice of using a choir for the words of groups (the High Priests, the four soldiers at the Cross, the mob, etc.) was centuries old. Under Protestantism, the Passion settings had gradually been expanded to include chorales, and later, arias, so that Bach's Passions contained no new element —except Bach's music.

Kuhnau, Bach's immediate predecessor in the leading Leipzig churches, had introduced the congregations to concerted Passion music with his St. Mark Passion in 1721, the year before he died. At the end of that same year, Prince Leopold of Anhalt-Cöthen, at whose court Bach held the post of Capellmeister, had taken a wife, and from then on his interest in music had so diminished that Bach thought it prudent to look about for other opportunities. The vacancy in the post of choir director to the Leipzig churches of St. Thomas and St. Nicholas, and chief musical instructor of boys in the choir school of St. Thomas, was such an opportunity, and during the fall and winter of 1722-1723 Bach was one of the candidates for that post. Undoubtedly he wrote the St. John Passion in Cöthen, with Leipzig in mind, and probably he first produced it on Good Friday, 1723,* at St. Thomas's, a few weeks before he was definitely elected by the Town Council.

In Bach's settings of the Passion story the singers represent three categories:

(1) The narrator (John or Matthew), who in his recitatives relates the story and connects and explains the dialogue of the protagonists;

(2) The characters in the drama, represented by recitatives for individuals and choral pieces for groups; and

(3) The congregation of believers, voicing their thoughts and emotions as they listen to the story and the lessons that should be taken to heart, in arias, chorales, and choral prologues and epilogues.

The artistic function of the pieces in this third category is to freeze the action for a time and sustain a mood, like the arias and concerted pieces in opera—and incidentally to give the listeners interludes of definite, sustained

*Or perhaps in 1724 at St. Nicholas's, after he was already installed. See p. xli.

rhythms and melodies to listen to, as a relief from too constant musical recitation.

But they served an even more important purpose, too. For the principal aim of the Passion settings—and Bach's unquestionable principal aim in writing them—was to teach a lesson: to make as vivid as possible to the Leipzig congregation the events portrayed, and to bring home to them immediately the moral to be drawn from each turn in the story and applied to their own lives. Bach's career and utterances show unmistakably that he considered music's highest purpose to be the service of religion; at his death his library contained eighty-one volumes on theological subjects.

III. Performing Forces

The Passions, like the Cantatas, were written for use in the church services for which it was Bach's principal duty to provide the music. To the Leipzig Town Council, Bach's employers, he addressed in 1730 a memorandum which he entitled: "Short but Most Necessary Draft for a Well-Appointed Church Music; with Certain Modest Reflections on the Decline of the Same". This memorandum is the most explicit source of much of our knowledge of the circumstances in which Bach worked. From it we learn that "Every musical choir should contain at least 3 sopranos, 3 altos, 3 tenors, and as many basses." The choir school had, at the time, 54 or 55 singers in all, and from among these there were four churches that had to be supplied with choirs. Moreover, Bach's memorandum summarized the boys' qualifications as follows: "Total: 17 usable, 20 not yet usable, and 17 unfit".

All the singers, of course, were male. They included boy sopranos and altos, and grown men who at some times sang tenor or bass parts and at others sang soprano and alto parts in falsetto. The "concertists" (soloists), "ordinarily 4 in number", sometimes took over certain sections of a choral piece, singing as a solo trio or quartet,* and then the difference between this solo group and the "tutti" effect of the full chorus was the difference between one singer on a part and three on a part, twelve being the usual total. (In the memorandum, Bach remarks that it would be "still better" if there could be sixteen.)

Bach probably did not try to keep separate the three categories of participants mentioned on p. iv as far as their singing representatives were concerned. His "concertists" probably sang along in what we should call the tutti music; they were the backbone of the choir. And his choir itself represented now the congregation (in the prologues, epilogues, and chorales), now the high priests, now the mob, now the soldiers gathered at the foot of the Cross. Perhaps some of his soloists assumed more than one role apiece. But his congregation of regular church-goers knew the stories well, and they were provided with printed texts to follow during the singing.

In modern practice, it is best to have six soloists: soprano, alto, two tenors (one for the Evangelist and one for the arias), and two basses (one for Jesus and one for the arias). From BG's description of the original parts (see p. 233), it is impossible to tell which tenor sang what. It seems not un-

---

*As for example perhaps in Nos. 1 and 67 of this work.

v

likely that Bach wrote Nos. 18 and 19 for the same tenor. And it is not always possible to find a single tenor who can sing both No. 19 and No. 32 well; but when it is possible, that is probably the best distribution. The tenor who sings No. 19 (if he is not the Evangelist) might well sing the little Peter recitatives in Nos. 14 and 18. The aria bass can sing the Pilate recitatives, and the smaller roles can be taken by chorus members. About the interpretation of the recitatives, see pp. xvi-xx, xxiii-xxvi, xxxv.

Every Sunday morning (except in Lent) Bach conducted his choir in the performance of a cantata with orchestra. The modern practice of accompanying the principal service of the week with organ only would have seemed shabby to the Leipzig congregation. Bach's memorandum tells us just how many instrumentalists he thought there should be:

2 or even 3 for the	Violin 1
2 or 3 for the	Violin 2
2 for the	Viola 1
2 for the	Viola 2
2 for the	Violoncello
1 for the	Bass Viol
2, or, if the piece requires, 3, for the	Oboe
1 or even 2 for the	Bassoon
3 for the	Trumpet
1 for the	Kettledrums

summa 18 persons at least, for the instrumental music.

N. B. If it happens that the church piece is composed with flutes also, whether they are *à bec* [recorders] or *Traversieri* [transverse flutes], as very often happens for variety's sake, at least 2 more persons are needed. Making altogether 20 instrumentalists.

Since the St. John Passion has no parts for trumpets, kettledrums, or second violas, the maximum number Bach had in mind for the orchestra of this work was from 15 to 17 players.

In addition, there was the keyboard player of the "continuo" or figured-bass part, who improvised above a given bass the harmonic background for the recitatives and for some arias, and a certain amount of harmonic and rhythmic "filling" in the pieces with orchestra accompaniment. The keyboard instrument used for this purpose was normally the organ, and only rarely and exceptionally did the harpsichord replace it.

The modern practice of using a harpsichord in concert performances of the Passions has little historical justification, whatever its aesthetic merits may be. (I have heard performances in which the presence of the harpsichord was in no way artistically disturbing; in fact, I used the harpsichord in my own performances of this and other choral works of Bach before I learned how the organ had been used in his time, and how, under favorable circumstances, it can be used effectively today.) There is little evidence that Bach used the harpsichord for the continuo in his religious music except as an emergency substitute, and much evidence that he did not. For one performance of the St. Matthew, a harpsichord part was made (and survives); but what is usually overlooked is that this harpsichord part takes the place only of the organ accompanying Chorus II, never of the one that accompanies the recitatives, which belong exclusively to Chorus I. The figured basses for the recitatives (and usually for everything else) were "realized" on the organ.*

What was the organ on which they were played? We need not concern ourselves with much of it, since only a few stops were used for continuo accompaniment. We know this from many sources. Perhaps the best one to quote here is Friedrich Erhardt Niedt's *Musicalische Handleitung zur Variation des Generalbasses* . . . in its second edition, revised by Mattheson and published in Hamburg in 1721, a year or so before the St. John Passion was written. Bach used the first volume of this work in his own teaching. This is what Niedt says (Chap. XI, §14):

Wenn nur eine oder zwo Stimmen singen oder spielen/ so brauche er im Manual bloss das Gedact 8 Fuss/und kein Pedal überall nicht; sind mehr Stimmen zu accompagniren/so kan er im Pedal Untersatz/oder Sub-Bass 16 Fuss mit dazu anziehen; wo aber ein Tenor, Alt, oder Discant-Zeichen stehet/ welches man sonst ein Bassetgen nennet/ so muss er das Pedal weglassen/ und die Noten eben in der Octave spielen/wo sie geschrieben stehen; hergegen/ fällt ein gantzer Chor von 8/12 oder mehr stimmen ein/ (wie dann in solchem Fall der Ort meistentheils mit den Wörtern *Chor/ tutti, ripieno* &c bezeichnet stehet) alsdann kann im Manual das achtfüssige Principal, und im Pedal/ zum Sub-Bass/noch eine Octava von 8 Fuss gezogen werden. Ist ein Stück mit Trompeten und Paucken gesetzet/ so wird im Pedal/ zur achtfüssigen Octava, ein Posaunen-Bass von 16. Fuss gezogen; die Töne müssen aber nicht bey gantzen oder halben Tächten ausgehalten werden/ sondern man darff sie nur ansprechen lassen.

When only one or two parts are singing or playing, he [the organist] should use only the 8′ Gedact, and no pedal at all anywhere; if more parts are to be accompanied, he can add in the pedal the *Untersatz* or sub-bass 16′; where, however, a tenor, alto, or soprano clef occurs, which makes what is called a *bassetto*, he must omit the pedal, and play the notes in the octave in which they are written; on the other hand, if a whole chorus of 8, 12, or more voices enters (in such a case the passage is usually marked with the words *Chorus, tutti, ripieno*, etc.), then in the manual the 8′ Principal and in the pedal, for the sub-bass, another 8′ Octava can be drawn. If a piece has trumpets and kettledrums, then in the pedal, in addition to the 8′ Octava, a 16′ trombone bass is drawn: but the tones must not be held out when values lasting a whole or half-measure occur, but rather they must be just allowed to speak [and then rest, instead of being sustained, as the notation would imply].

Many other writers throughout the 18th century agree on these points. The continuo accompaniment is to be played on soft stops, without any bright reeds or mixtures, with 8′ tone prevailing, perhaps occasionally punctuated with a touch of 16′ or brightened with a soft 4′. They are unanimous in cautioning against too much or too prominent organ tone. "Une voix qui chante doit toujours dominer; l'accompagnement n'est que pour l'orner et la soutenir [A singing voice must always predominate; the accompaniment is only for the purpose of ornamenting and supporting it]." So writes Dom Bédos de Celles in 1766. The greater the number of voices and instruments that take part, the more support the organ can give without stepping out of its subordinate role.

One can easily extend this clear principle, and state that the singing voice must always predominate over any instrument concerted with it, and any melodic instrument must always predominate over the merely harmonic

---

*This subject is discussed in the present writer's article "On the Keyboard Accompaniments to Bach's Leipzig Church Music" in the Musical Quarterly for July, 1950.

accompaniment played by the right hand of the organist from a figured bass (cf. p. xxviii ff.). The rank given to each member of the hierarchy varies with the character of the music: some pieces, and some passages, approach the chamber-music ideal of the equality of all participants, vocal and instrumental. But the principle is always valid, as far as it applies to the harmonic superstructure erected above the bass. The bass line itself, on the other hand, is a principal element in the musical texture, and the prominence given it by the organist must depend, as the 18th-century writers also agree, on the number and quality of bass instruments ('cello, bass viol, bassoon, contrabassoon) taking part. The 'cello or bass viol, or both, played the bass line throughout, being joined at times by bassoon or contrabassoon (see p. 234). The present-day organist is frequently at a disadvantage, having no stops at his disposal with which to make the bass line clear and definite without being obtrusive.*

It may be asked how the voices could predominate over the instruments when there were more instrumentalists in the orchestra than singers in the choir. There are several answers to this question. But the main point is this: we know from unanimous testimony that the voices *did* predominate in performances acceptable to 18th-century ears, as indeed they must have, since they carried the words, which in religious music particularly were all-important. It remains only to calculate how this result was achieved.

One factor that cannot be overlooked is that the stringed instruments in their original state (with shorter necks, flatter and lower bridges, smaller bass-bars, thinner strings, lower tension, and different bows) produced a good deal less volume than they have since they were remodeled for the express purpose of producing louder and more brilliant tones. The tone of oboes has perhaps not increased in the same proportion, but it has increased, as instrument-makers have learned to make the walls of the instrument thinner, and its inner diameter ("bore") correspondingly larger. It must be remembered, too, that these pieces were performed in a framework whose acoustic properties were different from those of our concert halls, and in a vaulted, stone church, oboes are far less obtrusive than in our carpeted auditoriums.

With modern instruments and an amateur chorus I have not found it possible to reproduce Bach's proportions with satisfying results. In many performances of his choral works, with an orchestra constituted exactly according to his specifications, I have had to use at least thirty-five or forty amateur singers. Present-day professional singers, on the other hand, produce a good deal more volume than Bach's singers, I am sure, so that a group of sixteen

---

*Most modern organs, not having been built with continuo accompaniment in mind, are ill-suited to it. One is faced with a choice among stops that are inaudible or too dull in concerted music and those that are too loud or too bright. And the pipes of the desired stops are often placed where the singers and instrumentalists can't hear them, or can't hear them on time, or where the audience hears them either more or less distinctly than the performers. There is also the pitch question. Instrumentalists not accustomed to playing with organ find it very uncomfortable to adjust to its inflexibility of pitch, and often the average pitch of the organ is uncomfortably low for them. In such circumstances, it would be pedantry not to prefer a harpsichord, or even a piano, utterly out of place as that instrument sounds in this music. A partial solution to this problem is offered by the Baldwin Electronic Organ, which I have used many times in preference to a pipe organ readily available. The Baldwin is easily tuned to any pitch; the speakers and console are easily movable; and the tone is readily adjusted both as to volume and (within limits) as to quality. When the speakers are so placed that the tone reaches the listeners by reflection (preferably several-fold) rather than directly, no one is conscious of anything unduly mechanical or "electronic" in the tone quality. Doubtless there are other electric organs equally well-suited to the task, as well as some that are not. I mention the Baldwin only because I have had no experience with any other, and because all the other solutions of the problem that I have tried have proved less satisfactory.

trained singers would make an excellent balance with an orchestra of about the same number. Both groups would sound louder than Bach's forces, I have no doubt, but perhaps in somewhat similar proportions.

When a symphony orchestra with sixty or more strings takes part in the performance of such a work, all the proportions are changed, and everything must be reconsidered. My own opinion is that such changes are not for the better, and I am convinced that while Bach might have delighted in the resources of the modern symphony orchestra, the music he would have written for it would have been designed to make the best use of those resources: he would not have welcomed the mere multiplication of having hundreds of performers do what could be done by several dozen. The fresco that covers the wall is not just an enlargement of the tempera painting on the altar panel. Bach's music is as full of eloquent detail as a panel painting, and it is no more improved, to my way of thinking, by performance with multiplied forces than a string quartet played by string orchestra, or a violin and piano sonata played by a dozen fiddlers and pianists. It is a delusion of our time that infinite refinement of detail is not compatible with breadth of conception, and that to be great a thing must be "great big". Even in our large concert halls* we do not resort to such distortions; and I think even in such surroundings it should be perfectly possible to readjust one's scale of dynamic values so as to be able to listen to Bach's music performed by such forces as he had in mind.

Nevertheless, the resources needed for performance of the Bach choral works, with the exacting demands they make on both singers and instrumentalists, are usually hard to find outside our symphony orchestras, and large-scale performances will probably continue to be in the majority for a long time to come. Many musicians and writers have jumped to the conclusion that since the symphony orchestra has five or six times as many strings as Bach had, the wood-winds must be multiplied in proportion (though as far as I know no one has suggested 15 trumpets and 5 pairs of kettledrums for the B Minor Mass). The fact is that music and arithmetic are not so simply connected. Sixty strings can play as softly as ten, and five flutes in unison do not sound five times as loud as one.

IV. Notation

The symbols by which Bach meant something different from the meanings attached to them today may be grouped under three heads: the rhythmic, the melodic, and the harmonic.

A. RHYTHMIC

1. Tempo

About 1500, metric notation seems to have provided a fairly reliable guide to tempo. We, on the other hand, have lost the feeling for any connection between the two. The eighth-note of the *Larghetto* of Beethoven's Second Symphony is about six times as long in actual duration as the eighth-note in the Scherzo (marked *Allegro*) of the same work, according to Beet-

---

*The Thomas-Kirche was a big building: about 80 feet wide, 140 feet long, and 140 feet high in the nave section; that is, slightly narrower than Carnegie Hall, but just as long and a good deal higher.

hoven's own metronome markings. Some of the Italian words originally used to describe the character of music have been relegated to the narrower and more specific task of indicating tempo alone; and composers have increasingly tended to give more or less precise metronome numbers as tempo indications, and let their choice of time-signatures be governed by other considerations.

Bach stands somewhere in the middle of this development: his time-signatures are not completely reliable guides to his tempo intentions, but they cannot be disregarded either. Only four movements of this work are marked in BG with verbal tempo indications at their beginnings: No 17, *Allegro;* No. 31, *Adagio;* No. 58, *Molto Adagio;* and No. 60, *Adagio.* Is this significant? Are these movements intended to be faster or slower than would be implied if they had no such markings? I think quite probably they are.

For most $\frac{4}{4}$ movements marked C, as well as for most $\frac{3}{4}$ movements, I believe that Bach had in mind a "medium" tempo—a "tempo ordinario"— of ♩ = 60–80 M.M., and that the tempo of eighth-notes, half-notes, etc., was roughly proportionate to this speed in many cases: ♪ = 120–160 in $\frac{3}{8}$ (i.e., ♩. = 40–54), with many exceptions, in which the tempo of $\frac{3}{8}$ seems no faster than that of the usual $\frac{3}{4}$); ♩ = 60–80 in ₵; ♩. = 30–40 in $\frac{6}{4}$ (i.e., ♩ = 88–120), etc. Many writers of the period associate beats with seconds; and some, notably Quantz (1752), following a tradition as old as Gafurius (1496), connect tempo with the pulse, for which Quantz sets the average speed at eighty to the minute. My impression is that this average speed (♩ = 60–80, and equivalents) applies without much qualification to Nos. 11, 13, 19, 34, 36, 38, 42, 44, 48, 50, 54, and 67, which are about half of the non-recitative movements of the St. John Passion.

No. 17 is marked *Allegro.* If Bach had been consistent in differentiating between C and ₵ he would doubtless have marked this movement ₵, which in general in his time meant twice as fast as C. But he was not, and apparently none of the manuscript sources for this number is in his handwriting anyway (see pp. 232 ff.). The measures seem to proceed in two halves rather than in four quarters, and the quarter-note seems about twice as fast as in No. 11 or No. 19. In No. 31, marked *Adagio,* it is the eighth-notes that seem to proceed at about the same speed as the quarters of Nos. 11, 19, etc., and the halves of No. 17. No. 58 is marked *Molto Adagio:* here the eighth-note is longer still—though perhaps not twice as long as in No. 31. *Alla breve,* which had no precise meaning as applied to $\frac{3}{4}$ meter, always meant relatively fast, and in No. 58 it indicates perhaps that the middle section goes not just twice but four times as fast as the *Molto Adagio* (♩ of the *Alla breve* = approximately ♪ of the *Molto Adagio*). No. 60 is marked *Adagio.* BG does not tell us where this marking occurs in the score or parts, but it clearly refers to the quarters of the C (= the dotted quarters of the $\frac{12}{8}$), which are probably not far from equal to the eighths of No. 58. The next-to-last measure of No. 62 is marked *Adagio,* and again this seems to mean about twice as slow as the C of the preceding measures.

This discussion seems to assume that the relations of two different tempi are always in the ratio of 1:2, which, of course, is not true. It was Quantz (1752) who tried to set up a scheme of tempi from slowest to fastest on that basis. But he concluded:

Was ich bisher gezeiget habe, trifft, wie schon oben gesaget worden, am genauesten und am allermeisten bey den Instrumentalstücken, als Concerten, Trio und Solo ein. Was die Arien im Italienischen Geschmacke anbelanget; so ist zwar wahr, dass fast eine jede von ihnen ihr besonderes Tempo verlanget. . . . Mit einer Kirchenmusik hat es eben dieselbe Bewandtniss, wie mit den Arien: ausgenommen, dass sowohl der Vortrag bey der Ausführung, als das Zeitmass, wenn es anders Kirchenmässig seyn soll, etwas gemässigter, als im Opernstyl genommen werden muss.

What I have here indicated applies, as has been said above, most precisely and generally to instrumental pieces, such as concertos, trios, and solos. As for arias in the Italian style, the truth is that almost every one of them demands its own particular tempo. . . . In church music the same holds true as in arias: except that both the style of performance and the tempo, if it is to be really suited to the church, must be somewhat more moderate than in opera style.

Every sensitive musician knows that there are many factors affecting tempo: the character and expressive quality of the music, technical limitations, the nature of the performing medium, the acoustics of the room in which the performance takes place, the degree of familiarity of the music to performer and listeners, and such intangible but often determining elements as mood, temperament, and so on. Nevertheless, Bach does not go to the extremes that Beethoven and later composers do: he never writes $\frac{3}{4}$ for a *presto* movement like a Beethoven Scherzo, or $\frac{9}{16}$ for an *adagio* like the one in Op. 111. Usually the beats in Bach's $\frac{3}{8}$ are faster than in his $\frac{3}{4}$. In the St. John Passion, the eighth-notes of Nos. 13 and 48 (both in $\frac{3}{8}$) seem to me a bit faster than the eighth-notes of Nos. 11 and 19 ($\frac{3}{4}$), making the beat a bit more than twice as fast. The words of both these $\frac{3}{8}$ movements express animation, and the emotional color of the words has always been a factor of recognized influence on tempo.

Similarly, the excitement inherent in the dramatic situation seems to call for a faster tempo in Nos. 3, 5, 23, 25, 29, and 46 than in the other movements marked C, though not twice as fast, as in No. 17. Or perhaps it would be more accurate to say that Bach's choice of the perpetual-motion figure in sixteenth-notes to express the excitement inherent in the situation calls for a faster tempo.

The denomination of the shortest note-values in a piece was also recognized as having a bearing on tempo. No. 17 has nò 16ths, another reason for taking its 8ths to be roughly equivalent to the 16ths of the $\frac{3}{4}$ and slower C movements. The perpetual-motion 16ths of Nos. 3, 5, etc., on the other hand, clearly serve a very different purpose from the expressive 16ths of Nos. 11, 19, etc. Finally, the expressive 32nds of No. 63 seem closely equivalent to the expressive 16ths of No. 11, so that here we have a $\frac{3}{8}$ in which the tempo of the beats is surely closer to that in the $\frac{3}{4}$ movements than to the other movements in $\frac{3}{8}$. Why Bach chose to write this movement in $\frac{3}{8}$ rather than $\frac{3}{4}$ remains unclear.

The 32nds of No. 32 are less uninterruptedly melodic than those of No. 63, and a $\frac{12}{8}$ measure at $\flat = $ 60–80 would be long indeed; it is unquestionably a slow piece, like several $\frac{12}{8}$ movements which Bach marked *Adagio* (e.g., the opening movement of the first gamba sonata). But the eighth-note cannot be as slow as in the $\frac{3}{8}$ of No. 63; even Bach does not expect the impossible, and when beats are grouped in twelves they cannot be as slow as when grouped in threes. Besides, No. 32 requires a singer with exceptional breath control. No matter at what tempo it is sung, and no matter how lightly of voice (to match the very soft accompaniment), few tenors will be able to avoid breaking the rainbow's arch (see pp. 102-106); but too slow a tempo would push the difficulties to impossible lengths.

When all is said and done, the choice of tempo must always remain partly a matter of personal taste and conviction.* Schweitzer well says: "The better a man plays Bach, the slower the tempo he dares adopt; the worse he plays, the faster he must take it . . . to give it at least some sort of interest." There are dangers in the other direction too, of course: those who have an uncomprehending "respect" for old music are apt to confuse dignity with dullness. A slow tempo cannot guarantee a poised performance any more than a fast tempo can guarantee a spirited one. Inner rhythmic tension to keep each piece alive from beginning to end, and sensitiveness to every inflection of the melody, harmony, rhythm, and instrumentation—these are the essentials for an ideal performance, whatever the tempo may be.

What is the use, then, of trying to find objective factors affecting the choice of tempo? None, if we expect to arrive at certain, simple, definite answers. But much, in certain cases, if we wish to increase our understanding of Bach's intentions. It is no use to adopt for performance, on the basis of historical evidence alone, a tempo of which one cannot become inwardly convinced. But sometimes historical evidence can throw new light on a piece, make us reconsider our choice, and show us the possibility of a tempo very different from what we had at first ("instinctively" as we like to flatter ourselves into believing) imagined.

2. Uneven notes; ♩· ♪ ; "2 against 3"; and "4 against 3"

There is an aspect of the notation of the 18th century and its interpretation that has been on the one hand too dogmatically treated by Dolmetsch, and on the other too long ignored by most of us. This is the question of "uneven notes".

Quantz (Chapter XI, § 12) writes:

Man muss unter den *Hauptnoten*, welche man auch: *anschlagende*, oder, nach Art der Italiäner, *gute* Noten zu nennen pfleget, und unter den *durchgehenden*, welche bey einigen Ausländern *schlimme* heissen, einen Unterschied im Vortrage zu machen wissen. Die Hauptnoten müssen allezeit, wo es sich thun lässt, mehr erhoben werden, als die durchgehenden. Dieser Regel zu Folge müssen die geschwindesten Noten, in einem jeden Stücke von *mässigem Tempo*, oder

One must know how to distinguish in performance between *principal* notes, also called "*initial*" or in the Italian usage *good* notes, on the one hand, and, on the other, "*passing*" notes, called by some foreigners *bad* notes. The principal notes must wherever possible be brought out more than the passing ones. [Quantz, of course, uses the term "passing notes" only in the sense of metrically weak ones, not in the sense of dissonant non-chord tones.] In accordance with this rule, the fastest notes

---

*After considering all of the foregoing more or less objective factors, I have set down for each movement the fastest and slowest tempo I could imagine adopting with conviction, under varying circumstances. It is also only fair to state that in almost every instance the fastest tempo I could imagine taking, in the winter of 1949-1950, was slower than the tempo I had noted down as the actually desirable one the last time I had conducted a performance of the work, in the spring of 1946. But one always needs to keep in mind the remark of Debussy to his publisher Durand about metronome markings: " . . they are valid for just one measure."

auch im *Adagio*, ungeachtet sie dem Gesichte nach einerley Geltung haben, dennoch ein wenig ungleich gespielet werden; so dass man die anschlagenden Noten einer jeden Figur, nämlich die erste, dritte, fünfte, und siebente, etwas länger anhält, als die durchgehenden, nämlich, die zweyte, vierte, sechste, und achte: doch muss dieses Anhalten nicht so viel ausmachen, als wenn Puncte dabey stünden. Unter diesen geschwindesten Noten verstehe ich: die Viertheile im Dreyzweytheiltacte; die Achttheile im Dreyviertheil—und die Sechzehntheile im Dreyachttheiltacte; die Achttheile im Allabreve; die Sechzehntheile oder Zwey und dreyssigtheile im Zweyviertheil—oder im gemeinen geraden Tacte: doch nur so lange, als keine Figuren von noch geschwindern oder noch einmal so kürzen Noten, in jeder Tactart mit untermischet sind; denn alsdenn müssten diese letztern auf die oben beschriebene Art vorgetragen werden. Z. E. Wollte man . . . die acht Sechzehntheile unter den Buchstaben (k) (m) (n) langsam in einerley Geltung spielen;

in every piece *in moderate tempo,* or in *Adagio,* despite the fact that they have in appearance the same value, must nevertheless be played a little unevenly. Thus the "initial" notes of every group, namely the first, third, fifth, and seventh, must be held somewhat longer than the "passing" ones, namely the second, fourth, sixth, and eighth. But this holding must not amount to as much as it would if there were dots after the notes. By the fastest notes I mean: quarters in $\frac{3}{2}$; eighths in $\frac{3}{4}$ and sixteenths in $\frac{3}{8}$; eighths in *Alla breve;* sixteenths or thirty-seconds in $\frac{2}{4}$ or C; but only so long as no groups of notes twice as fast or once again as short are intermingled, in whatever meter, for then these last-named would have to be performed in the manner described above.

For example, if one were to play the eight 16th-notes in each of the following groups slowly and evenly:

(k)   (m)   (n)

so würden sie nicht so gefällig klingen, als wenn man von vieren die erste und dritte etwas länger, und stärker im Tone, als die zweyte und vierte, hören lässt. Von dieser Regel aber werden ausgenommen: erstlich die geschwinden Passagien in einem sehr geschwinden Zeitmaasse, bey denen die Zeit nicht erlaubet sie ungleich vorzutragen, und wo man also die Länge und Stärke nur bey der ersten von vieren anbringen muss. Ferner werden ausgenommen: alle geschwinden Passagien welche die Singstimme zu machen hat, wenn sie anders nicht geschleifet werden sollen: denn weil jede Note von dieser Art der Singpassagien, durch einen gelinden Stoss der Luft aus der Brust, deutlich gemachet und markiret werden muss; so findet die Ungleichheit dabey keine Statt. Weiter werden ausgenommen: die Noten über welchen Striche oder Puncte stehen, oder von welchen etliche nach einander auf einem Tone vorkommen; ferner wenn über mehr, als zwo Noten, nämlich, über vieren, sechsen, oder achten ein Bogen steht; und endlich die Achttheile in Giguen. Alle diese Noten müssen egal, das ist, eine so lang, als die andere, vorgetragen werden.

they would not sound so pleasing as they would if the first and third were held somewhat longer, and played somewhat louder, than the second and fourth. This rule has the following exceptions: first, fast passages in a very fast tempo, in which there is not enough time for them to be performed unevenly, and in which accordingly only the first of each four notes can be emphasized in loudness and length. Also excepted are all fast passages for the singing voice, when they are not to be slurred; for every note in this type of vocal passage must be marked and made clear by a gentle expulsion of air from the chest, and thus unevenness has no place in such passages. Further exceptions occur: when notes have dashes or dots over them, or when there are several successive notes of the same pitch; also when there is a slur over more than two notes—that is, over four, six, or eight; and finally concerning 8th-notes in gigues. All these notes must be played even, that is, one as long as the other.

Since Quantz lists a certain number of exceptions, we cannot doubt that he means that unevenness should prevail in virtually all circumstances not included among his exceptions. The tradition of uneven performance of pairs of apparently equal notes goes back at least as far as the middle of the 16th century, and the convention persisted here and there into the early 19th century. How great the difference between the two notes should be, whether the first or the second note should be the longer, and under what circumstances —these are questions on which unanimity has never obtained, and at this distance it is hard to answer them. Apart from Quantz's unequivocal remarks, there are few clear references to the practice outside France; but the very absence of such references has been taken to mean that the convention was so completely "understood" that it was considered too obvious to need description.

Mr. Sol Babitz, of Los Angeles, believes that in this convention we have a key to a whole world of what he calls "expressive rhythm"—a world that remains locked to us until we use this key.

It is easy to see one of the reasons why such unevenness was not clearly notated: it would have been far too complicated. French writers of the 18th century tell us that the uneven lengths of the two notes of each pair might at

times be related in ratios as uneven as 3:1 (♩. ♪ or ♪♪.) or as nearly even as 7:5 (-♪♪.♪ or ♪♪♪.), with ratios of moderate unevenness in between: 5:3 (♪♪♩. or ♪.♪♪), 3:2 (♪.♩ or ♪♪.), or 2:1 (♪♩ or ♪♪).In addition,

the convention of uneven notes implied greater freedom in performance than such precise and complicated notation would have permitted.

But if we *arbitrarily and purely for the sake of illustration* choose the 3:2 ratio, we can imagine its application in such cases as the following:

xiv

(Here the contrasting interpretations of ♪♩ [long-short] and of ♪♪ [short-

long] certainly provide a welcome explanation of Bach's varying notation of the appogiaturas in measures 49, 51, 53, and 55, otherwise difficult to account for.)

No. 63, m. 1

Flutes and English Horns

Org. and Continuo

etc.

I think it is undeniable that at least some of these examples do embody a more "expressive rhythm" than the even interpretations we are used to. This is not the place to discuss in detail the evidence for and against unevenness. I hope Mr. Babitz will soon set forth in print his persuasive arguments. Meanwhile, the little that has been said here will indicate the nature of the problem, and will show that it has connections with our interpretation of appogiatura notation and with our choice of tempo. (Expressive unevenness of short notes obviously calls for slower tempi, in some instances, than would be needed without it.)

Another respect in which the metric notation of Bach's time differs from ours concerns the patterns ♩. ♩ , ♩. ♪♪ , etc. Many writers of the 18th century tell us that where such rhythms occur frequently and prominently, they are to be pointed up by lengthening the value of the dotted notes (or inserting rests after them), and making the short notes much shorter and later than a literal interpretation of the notation would indicate. (See Nos. 19 and 58 of this work.) When ♩. ♩ occurs simultaneously with ♩♩♩ or ♩♩♩ in compound meter, Quantz tells us that the dotted rhythm must be exaggerated as usual, so that the 16th comes well after the third 8th. Marpurg (1755) says just the opposite: either ♩. ♩ or ♩♩ occurring simultaneously with ♩♩♩ is to be performed ♩ ♪ . Philipp Emanuel Bach, the most frequently quoted authority on this point, is ambiguous, or at least his words have been taken to point more clearly in one direction than they really do. He says that on a keyboard instrument the differentiation desired by Quantz is "often unpleasant, and always difficult [*oft unangenehm, allezeit aber schwer*]". This passage is the most widely quoted statement on the subject and it is almost universally taken to mean much more than it says. But it carries no implication that ♪. ♪♪ must *always* be softened into ♪ ♪ ♪ even at the keyboard—much less when two or more performers are involved. In a movement like No. 60 of this work, I see no reason why ♩♩ and ♩♩♩ should not be performed just as written: "2 against 3" and "4

xv

against 3" are effective rhythmic devices in Bach as elsewhere. As for ♩. ♩ in this movement, it may well be sung as ♩♫ if not as ♩.. ♩ . (The Sanctus of the B Minor Mass and Verse 6 of the Cantata *Christ lag in Todesbanden* present similar problems, which I should solve in the same way.)

3. *Long notes played short*

A third convention of metric notation is mentioned at the end of the quotation from Niedt, on p. vii: "the tones must not be held out when values lasting a whole or half-measure occur, but rather they must be just allowed to speak." This remark of Niedt's does not refer specifically to recitative, but on the contrary seems to apply principally to the use of the organ in concerted music. We do have, as will be seen shortly, explicit descriptions of the practice described in connection with recitative, and we cannot doubt that it was customary there. Philipp Emanuel Bach says:

Bey einem Recitative mit aushaltenden begleitenden Instrumenten bleibet man auf der Orgel blos mit der Grundnote im Pedale liegen, indem man die Harmonie bald nach dem Anschlage mit den Händen aufhebet. Die Orgeln sind selten rein gestimmet, und folglich würde die Harmonie zu den erwehnten Recitativen, welche oft chromatisch ist, sehr widrig klingen, und sich mit der Begleitung der übrigen Instrumente gar nicht vertragen.

In a recitative with accompanying instruments playing sustained tones, the organist sustains only the bass in the pedals, and lifts his hands just after striking the chords. Organs are seldom purely tuned, and accordingly the harmony in this kind of recitative, which is often chromatic, would sound very ugly, and would not agree at all with the accompaniment of the other instruments.

Emanuel is not concerned, in the chapter in which this occurs, with anything but recitative.

But the reason he gives applies with the same force to J. S. Bach's concerted pieces. And there are other reasons equally cogent. A sustained organ part, playing a four-part chorale texture as an accompaniment to concerted instruments and voices, is constantly in the way. Even apart from questions of intonation, it constantly muddies the texture and obscures the hierarchy of stronger and weaker beats and parts of beats that is essential to this music (and explicitly described as essential by many writers of the period). The continuo accompaniment should enhance the rhythm, not spoil it. Quantz states it as a rule that in harpsichord accompaniment in general, quarters are to be played as 8ths, and 8ths as 16ths. Leopold Mozart gives similar instructions for playing the string accompaniment to a solo. Emanuel Bach says that in his harpsichord solo sonatas, notes not marked with either staccato dots or slurs, particularly quarters and 8ths in moderate tempi, are to be sustained for only half of their time-value. If this was true in the 1750s, when all these men wrote, it was probably even truer in the 1720s. For in the interval, notation had become considerably more explicit and legato-playing more common, the latter partly as a result of J. S. Bach's own example in solo-playing at the organ and clavier.

As for recitative accompaniment, the practice of playing the organ chords short was not at all confined to those recitatives in which other instruments participated in the accompaniment. It is described in connection with accompaniment by organ and bass instruments only, in 1772, by Christoph Gottlieb Schröter:

Es giebt dreyerley Arten des Recitativs. Das Kennzeichen der ersten Art ist, wenn man über den Bassnoten mit Signaturen auch eine Singestimme, NB. ohne Beywort: *Accompagnement* oder *col stromenti* erblicket. Obgleich der Bass hier meistentheils ganze und halbe Tacte Noten hat; so muss doch der Organist jegliche solche langweiligen Noten nebst denen erforderten harmonischen Griffen fast wie ein 8tel kurz abstossen.

There are three kinds of recitatives. The first kind may be recognized by the fact that above the bass notes with their figures a vocal part is written, without the remark *Accompagnement*, or *col stromenti*. Although the bass in such cases is written mostly in half and whole notes, nevertheless the organist must play all such long notes, together with the harmonies prescribed, detached and almost like 8th-notes.

This practice is described by many writers from one end of the 18th century to the other. Johann David Heinichen, in his *Neuerfundene und Gründliche Anweisung* (1711), shows that it was applied at the discretion of the organist:

Die Manier und Weise aber/ das Recitativ wohl zu tractiren/ ist denen Instrumenten nach/ worauf es tractiret wird/ auch sehr unterschieden. In Kirchen-Recitativ, da man mit nachklingenden und summenden Pfeiff-Werck zu thun hat/ braucht es eben keiner Weitläufftigkeiten/ denn man schläget die Noten meist nur platt nieder/ und die Hände bleiben hierbey ohne weiteres Ceremoniel so lange liegen/ bis ein anderer Accord folget mit welchen es wiederum/ wie zuvor/ gehalten wird.

Hebet man aber ja die Hände so gleich wieder auf/ nach Anschlagung eines neuen Accordes, und machet statt der Noten gleichsam eine Pause, so geschiehet solches nach Gelegenheit der Umstände/ entweder den Sänger/ oder die bissweilen zum Recitativ accompagnirende Instrumenta besser zu hören/ und zu observiren. Oder man findet auch andere Raison, die Hände z. E. deswegen in etwas aufzuheben/ weil etwan jezuweilen in Basse 3/4. und mehr Tacte in einem Tone und Accord liegen bleiben/ und folgbar das Gehöre durch das in einerley Tone stetig summende Pfeiff-Werck kan verdriesslich gemachet werden. Welches alles dem Judicio und Gefallen eines Accompagnisten heimgestellt bleibet.

The manner and nature of the proper treatment of the recitative, however, varies greatly according to the instruments on which it is played. In church recitatives, since one has to do with organ-pipes which hum and continue to sound, no elaborations are needed, for one just puts the keys down flatly [i.e., not arpeggiated, as on the harpsichord], and the hands remain lying on the keys without further ceremony until another chord follows, which is held out in its turn.

When, on the other hand, the hands are lifted at once from the keys, immediately after striking a new chord, so that a rest takes the place of the notes, this is done according to the circumstances obtaining, the better to hear and observe either the singer or the instruments that sometimes accompany the recitative. Or some other reason is found to lift the hands somewhat, as for example, the fact that sometimes the bass remains upon one note and chord for 3, 4, or more measures, and consequently the steady, monotonous tone of the humming organ-pipes becomes irksome to the ear. All these questions must be settled by the taste and judgment of the accompanist.

In Bach's own time, one C. Voigt, one of the few writers of the period who refers to Bach as a church musician, says in his *Gespräch von der Musik* (1742):

Ich muss aber nicht beständig dabey liegen bleiben, und eine Leyer daraus machen, sonst wäre es kein Accompag. nein, sondern ich muss die Hände fein aufheben damit die Zuhörer den Text wohl versehen können.

However I must not let my hands lie continuously on the keys, droning away like a hurdy-gurdy,* for that would not be an accompaniment, but I must lift them properly so that the listeners can well understand the text.

---

*The hurdy-gurdy referred to is not the street instrument we know today, of course, but the old mechanical string instrument with drone strings.

Bach explicitly illustrates this practice in several works of which the "original" continuo parts date from his later years, when he tended to make his notation increasingly explicit, perhaps because his performers belonged to a generation that was beginning to forget the old conventions.*   Such works include, for example, Cantatas 94 and 97, and most conspicuously the St. Matthew Passion, from which the following excerpt is taken.

There is no explicit proof that he followed the same practice in the St. John Passion, as far as we can tell from the description of the sources in BG. But it seems entirely likely that he did.   Once it is understood, it recommends itself so strongly on musical and aesthetic grounds that one cannot understand why one did not deduce it from the purely internal evidence of the music itself.

"The Recitative originated about 1600", we read in the reference books. But there must have been a practice of *parlando* narrative-singing punctuated by strummed chords on a stringed instrument for thousands of years.   What was new in 1600 must have been the incorporation of this practice into "art music", and specifically the attempt to capture it in metric notation.   On the kitharas, harps, lutes, guitars, and other plucked instruments originally used for accompanying narratives, the sound of the punctuating chords would die away rapidly, whether the player thought of them as long or short in time-value.   When they were first notated, there was no reason to write | ♪ ⁊ 𝄾 ▬ | , when | 𝅝 | would be so much less trouble, and on plucked instruments the effect would be the same.   When the accompaniment was transferred to the organ, the notation was not changed.   But many musicians must have de-

---

*Even in an earlier work, Cantata No. 18, *Gleich wie der Regen und Schnee* (1713 or 1714), the original bassoon part for the bass of the first recitative is written in short notes, perhaps because a particular player unused to playing recitative accompaniments was involved.

cided that to play the long notes on the organ as notated tended to obscure the recitation, and that to obtain the punctuating effect one must in general promptly lift the hand from the keys, as described by Schröter and Heinichen.

Whatever the true history of this convention may be, the fact that it has been so long forgotten, and that recitatives in sacred music are so often sung against sustained organ tone, is largely responsible, I am sure, for the dull, "churchy" style in which they are customarily delivered. Such a style obscures all the narrative interest of the story—which is what recitative was made for—in favor of that stuffy Sunday atmosphere which an irreligious age thinks of as religious, but which is as far as possible from the vividness that the Biblical narratives had for such genuinely religious composers as Schütz and Bach. Nothing will do more to restore that narrative vividness to their works than to play the chords short, and thus leave the Evangelist singing out into a silent church or auditorium. He will feel lonesome at first, and this will lead him to reach out and make a real contact with his listeners, as any true narrator must, rather than rob the recitative of all its life and pace by merely going through the motions of piously intoning something that in its unending *sostenuto* is not complete as pure music.*

Just how long each chord should be sustained must be left to individual interpreters. In this edition, the right-hand chords are mostly notated as 8th-notes. This, too, is a convention, and does not mean that the chords must be uniformly dry and staccato; their length must vary. My purpose in leaving the notation of the bass untouched is to leave it open to those who do not accept the described convention to interpret Bach's notation as they prefer. It appears here exactly as in BG, with the exception of occasional octave transpositions for purely practical reasons. In the 18th century some musicians actually did sustain the bass tones while playing the right-hand chords short. But from what evidence is known to me, it seems likely that Bach intended the bass tones to be short, too.

In the St. Matthew Passion, the words of Jesus are accompanied throughout by sustained string tone, until the final "Eli, eli". Here the organ, which has accompanied all the other recitatives in detached style, suddenly has sustained chords to take the place of the silent strings, which, apparently intended by Bach to represent the watchful omnipresence of God-the-Father, now forsake Jesus in accordance with the text. At this point he is "crying with a loud voice". For the restrained speech which he always employs until this moment, string tone is more manageable, dynamically, than organ tone. It can be soft enough not to obscure the words and yet be distinctly heard. And while to vary the dynamics of the organ accompaniment in accordance with the inflections of the voice is against the nature of the instrument, and impossible without an obtrusive "pumping" of the swell-pedal (which Bach's organ did not even possess), string instruments naturally increase and diminish the volume of sound easily, flexibly, and unobtrusively, as the musical expression varies. In the St. John Passion, Jesus, like the other characters, is accompanied only by the organ and bass instruments. I do not recommend fully sustained organ background for his words, in imitation of the string accompaniment of the St. Matthew. A good singer can make them fully

---

*The foregoing paragraph is quoted almost verbatim from the prefatory remarks to the present editor's edition of the Schütz *Christmas Story* (New York, G. Schirmer, Inc., 1949).

impressive with no more support than is given to the other recitative singers. (Particularly a passage like "Stecke dein Schwert in die Scheide", in No. 8, mm. 11 and 12, is more effective without any sustaining harmony than with it.) Nevertheless, the recitatives of Jesus are on the whole closer than the other recitatives to the arioso style, and the accompaniments for them might well be played in more sustained fashion than is here indicated (perhaps also with some difference of registration).

The essence of recitation is freedom—freedom to make the narration sound natural and convincing. All the writers of the period stress this point, which would be self-evident even if they did not: the metric notation is a mere outline of the rhythm; the singer is to be free to bend it as he needs to, to make the narration live. The same must be true of the accompaniment: the organist and the singer must fully understand each other's purpose, and the texture of the organ accompaniment must vary—now dry and detached, now more sustained—as the nature of the music and the expression vary. The notation here given is no more than a framework for that varying texture.

4. Holds in Chorales

It was customary in congregational singing in the 17th and 18th centuries to prolong the final tone of each line in the hymns. During this prolongation, the competent organist frequently improvised a brief cadenza leading into the next phrase. But it is doubtful whether the congregation joined in singing the chorales of Bach's Passions, and unlikely that any such cadenzas were improvised during their course.

The manuscripts of Bach's choral works, autograph and otherwise, contain the fermatas almost throughout. It may well be that he intended them to be observed. A comparison of Nos. 7 and 27 of this work furnishes some evidence that he did: both have the same Crüger tune, and their texts are respectively the seventh stanza and the eighth and ninth stanzas of Johann Heermann's hymn *Herzliebster Jesu*. But No. 7 has a fermata on the fourth note, while No. 27 has none till the end of the first line of the stanza. This would indicate that Bach wished to underline the meaning of the text by prolonging the word "*Lieb'*".

Sometimes, however, he wrote fermatas at the ends of hymn-lines simply out of habit or in deference to convention, in places where he cannot have intended the rhythmic flow to be halted. Instances of this are plentiful in the *Orgelbüchlein*. One of the most striking occurs in the chorale *Erschienen ist der herrliche Tag*, in which the chorale tune appears in canon between the top and bottom parts at the interval of one measure, and fermatas are written at the end of each line in both the canonic parts.

A century earlier (1628) Schütz wrote in the introduction to his *Psalmen Davids:*

Fürs Andere/ hab ich an Statt der Pausen mich der Strichlein zu Ende eines jeglichen Verssleins darumb gebrauchen sollen/ weil doch in derogleichen *genere compositionis* die Pausen nicht eigentlich observiret werden. . . .	For the rest, I have thought it better to use a little line at the end of each verse, instead of a pause, since of course in this sort of composition the pauses are not really observed.

There is no categorical answer to this question, it seems to me. One cannot say that it is wrong to observe the fermatas, or wrong to disregard them. In performance, Bach may well have held some of them and disregarded others.

B. MELODIC (Ornamentation)

Eighteenth-century performing musicians, as everyone knows, were in the habit of altering the melodic lines notated for them, by adding many sorts of ornaments. Some of these ornaments were indicated in the music by small notes or other special signs. Others were definitely implied, or depended on the discretion of the performer.

Writers of this period liked to compare ornamentation in music to seasoning in food, many of them pointing out that both are best used in moderation. We may carry the parallel a little further: seasoning may be added to food either by the cook (composer) or at the table (in performance). Bach's music is more like the food that has been well-seasoned by the cook; Handel's (and that of many of his contemporaries) is often like the greens and herbs that will make a fine salad when a good dressing is extemporized for them at the table. But just as a good salad-dressing has to be made up on the spot and is never twice exactly the same, so the ornaments for 18th-century music must often have an improvisatory character, even when, as sometimes in Bach, the composer has indicated just where (but not just how) he wants them added.

In the famous criticism of Bach published by his contemporary, Scheibe, in 1737, one of the reproaches leveled at Bach was that "every ornament, every little grace, and everything that one thinks of as belonging to the method of playing, he expresses completely in notes; and this not only takes away from his pieces the beauty of harmony but completely covers the melody throughout".

It would be easy to misunderstand this statement. First of all, we must remember that it may not represent Bach's own point of view. It is true that the reply to it, made by Birnbaum, doubtless with Bach's approval, does not dispute the allegation, but defends the practice on the ground that too many performers are ill-equipped to devise their own ornaments in good taste. But we must understand that this whole dispute concerns only *some* of Bach's works, in which he did write out or indicate all or almost all of the melodic elaborations usually left, in his time, to the performer: pieces like the slow movement of the Italian Concerto, or the organ chorales *Nun komm' der Heiden Heiland* and *O Mensch, bewein' dein' Sünde gross*. These were among the comparatively few works of which Bach carefully prepared a "final version" for publication or otherwise—and in which he took pains to make details clear to the stranger into whose hands a copy might come.

Bach was well known, during his lifetime, only as a great keyboard performer and composer, and some of his keyboard music had already circulated fairly widely. But the vast majority of his works—the St. John Passion among them—were not published in his time, and were not written or prepared by him for publication. They were written simply for his own use, for performance by him or under his direction; and what was not included in the notation could be imparted orally, or was understood by the performers as a matter of course.

Even in such works, it is true, Bach wrote out details that many of his contemporaries would have left to the performer. Accordingly, there is, in general, much less room in his music for added detail than there is in theirs. In this edition, the very few ornaments that have been added by the editor are clearly identified by brackets. They consist mostly of trills at cadences corresponding to other cadences in the same pieces bearing trills in the original manuscripts, or appoggiaturas in similar circumstances.

Because of the essentially improvisatory character of trills, appoggiaturas, and other ornaments, the attempt to write out just what metric value each tone is to have can never be successful. I think this may be partly what Scheibe meant in criticizing Bach for writing out so much, and if he objected to Bach's methods one can imagine what he and every other 18th-century musician would have said about the modern editor's attempt to make explicit what even Bach despaired of notating. The many tables of ornament notation and execution that have come down to us are far from unanimous even on the melodic shape of some ornaments, and most of them do not even attempt precise metric indications. The suggestions made in this edition for the metric shape of trills and appoggiaturas are in no sense binding, or definite, or even accurate. What makes a performer convincing is always the illusion of spontaneous—in this sense, improvisatory—expression he is able to create, and the attempt to pin down the rhythm of living music at all in the crudely simple arithmetical ratios of notated meter is only a degree closer to the possible than the attempt to notate those most elusive of all musical configurations: ornaments.

1. Appoggiaturas

(a) IN CONCERTED MUSIC

Of the many 18th-century rules for the realization of ornaments, few can be applied generally to the works of Bach. The rule, for example, that the appoggiatura normally takes half the metric value of the note it precedes (or two-thirds if that note is dotted), with its various corollaries, can rarely be made to fit Bach's music. Attempts to apply it dogmatically lead too often to musical absurdities. Emanuel's rule that the metric value of the appoggiatura is indicated by the notation of the appoggiatura itself applies mainly to his own works—not at all to his father's. Where J. S. Bach is concerned, I have found much more helpful the remark of J. G. Walther (in his *Lexicon,* under ACCENTO) that the appoggiatura takes

der folgenden Note an ihrer Geltung manchmahl nur etwas weniges: als in den grössern Noten; manchmahl aber, und zwar in den kleinern, die Helffte.	sometimes only a small part of the value of the following note: as when that note is one of the longer values; sometimes, on the other hand, when the notes are short, half the value.

The rules that apply to Bach's appoggiaturas in this work are, it seems to me, as follows:

1. *The appoggiatura almost always occurs on the strong beat or strong part of the beat, taking its value from the note that follows.* The practice of the 19th and 20th centuries is so generally opposite to this, as far as notes written in small size are concerned, and our singers and players are so in the habit

of performing "grace-notes" before the beat, i.e., taking the value of the ornament from the preceding note, that I have chosen to err on the dogmatic side, and have indicated realizations of the appoggiatura in accordance with the above rule in every case, although in a few instances there is room for possible disagreement (e.g., No. 63, m. 67).

2. *The appoggiatura is always legato with the tone that follows, and usually detached from the tone that precedes it.*

3. *The appoggiatura*, which is usually dissonant, acquires a certain stress from that fact alone. It *usually requires little or no conscious accentuation as compared with the tone that precedes it; but however little accent it receives, the tone that follows must receive still less.* That is, the scheme is always ♪ but had best not be thought of as ♩ | ♪ .

4. (This rule is my own formulation of what seems to me implied between the lines of 18th-century writing; I cannot give any explicit 18th-century authority for it except one passage in Emanuel Bach (I, ii, ii, § 14; English, p. 92), which does not set up any general rule. Writings of the 18th century on "les notes inégales" provide many examples of similar instructions for analogous cases, but not specifically for appoggiaturas.) *Frequently* in passages where the beat is regularly divided into halves, quarters, etc., *the appoggiatura* had better take something like one-third or two-thirds, or two-fifths or three-fifths, of the value of the following note,

rather than half: e.g., **C** ♪ (♪ ♪♪♪♪) to be played ♪♪ or ♪♪ or ♪♪. or ♪.♪ rather than ♪♪ . That is, it *had better seem to be quite independent of the regular metric subdivisions.*

N. B. The varying notation of the appoggiaturas in this edition, now in small notes, now in the little slur-like marks, follows exactly the notation in BG. The BG editor used the small notes for appoggiaturas he took from the "original" score, and the slur-like marks for those from the "original" parts. Keeping this in mind, the reader can tell which appoggiaturas probably have the authority of Bach's own handwriting by consulting pp. 232-234. But, of course, even in pages in Bach's handwriting, ornaments may have been added by others, at Bach's direction or on their own initiative, under his supervision or after his death. And there is no point in being too literal in this matter, since undoubtedly some appoggiaturas were "understood" in Bach's day, and there was no need to indicate them.

(b) IN RECITATIVES

The use of the appoggiatura in recitatives is a separate question; indeed, the word appoggiatura frequently means something quite different in recitatives, involving not the addition of a tone not notated, or notated in small size, but rather the substitution for a notated tone of another and different tone, sometimes a second and sometimes a fourth above the notated tone. The conventions governing such usages are set forth in the preface to G. P. Telemann's *Harmonischer Gottesdienst*, dated Hamburg, 1725. (Telemann's remarks are summarized and discussed by Spitta in his Bach biography [German Vol. II, pp. 142–43; English Vol. II, pp. 311–12]). A generation later (in 1757), the conventions were described again by Johann Friedrich Agricola, who had been a pupil of J. S. Bach in Leipzig. Since Telemann's remarks are already available in Spitta, while Agricola's are not so easy to find, and not translated, I quote the latter. The two men agree in substance: Agricola's examples, with Italian words, are similar to Telemann's with German ones, showing that the convention had not changed during the thirty-year interval. In fact, it is one of the few elements of Bach style that has come down more or less unchanged through the centuries as part of "tradition", doubtless owing to the fact that it belonged to opera, some of whose tradition goes back in a continuous line to the 17th century, as well as to Handel's oratorios, some of which have been performed continually since they were written. Other practices belonging to Bach's performing style were forgotten almost immediately upon his death, so that most Bach tradition dates from the period of Zelter and Mendelssohn, and has little to do with Bach's own practice.

Agricola writes:

Der Gebrauch bringt mit sich, dass in allen dreyen Arten des Recitativs einige Noten verändert werden, einige hingegen einen kleinen Zusatz bekommen: welches aber doch im Kirchen und Kammer-Recitativ häufiger als im theatralischen angebracht werden kann.

1) Die Recitativcadenzen werden gemeiniglich so ausgeschrieben (a): man singt aber die vorletzte Note eine Quarte höher, und wiederholet also die vorhergehende (b). Einige Componisten pflegen sie auch so zu schreiben wie man sie singt. Endiget sich aber eine solche Cadenz mit einer einzigen langen Sylbe; so macht man vor der letzten Note nur einen Vorschlag aus der Quarte von oben (c).

Custom has it that in all three kinds of recitative some notes are changed, while additions are made to others: and this applies more frequently to church and chamber than to theater recitatives.

1) Recitative cadences are usually written thus (a): but the note before the last is sung a fourth higher, thus repeating the preceding note (b). Some composers habitually write them as they are sung. But if such a cadence ends with a single long syllable, one inserts before the last note only an appoggiatura from the fourth above (c).

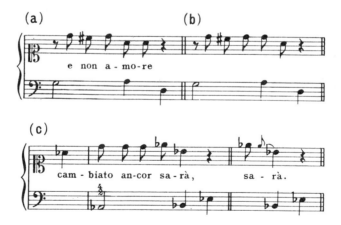

This point 1 we can pass over quickly: Bach is one of the composers who habitually writes recitative cadences not like (a) but like (b), that is, as they are to be sung. As for (c), Bach usually writes this out in full, too; there are several examples in this work. In the "original" manuscript part for the Evangelist (not in Bach's handwriting), the end of the Recitative No. 10

reads: ♩ The "original" manuscript score (also not in Bach's

für das Volk

handwriting at this point) reads: ♩ . It is easy to be too sure

für das Volk

what such differences mean; perhaps this one is inadvertent. But the word *Volk* is a short syllable, and undoubtedly the more direct ending on the one tone is more effective here.

Agricola continues:

2) Vor einer Note die einen anschlagenden Terzensprung herab macht, absonderlich wenn ein kurzer Einschnitt, der ein Komma oder anderes Unterscheidungszeichen ausdrücket, darauf folget, pflegt man zuweilen entweder einen Vorschlag aus der Secunde von oben anzubringen, denselben auch wohl, in zärtlichen Stellen, mit einem leisen Pralltriller zu begleiten (d): oder man setzet, zumal wenn noch eine Note nachkömmt die auf eben demselben Tone bleibt, an Stellen die nicht affectuos sind, anstatt der ersten Note nur den Vorschlag (e). Ein gleiches kann man, in ähnlichen Fällen, auch anbringen, wenn die zwo Noten anstatt der Terze nur eine Secunde fallen (f).

2) Before the second note of a downward leap of a third, when that note occurs on a strong beat, especially when it is followed by a brief caesura, representing a comma or other punctuation mark, it is customary either to introduce an appoggiatura from the second above, even adding to this, in tender passages, a light Pralltriller (d), or else, particularly when another note on the same pitch follows, in passages that are not expressive, simply to substitute the appoggiatura for the first of the two identical notes (e). The same things can be done, in similar instances, when the downward melodic interval is only a second, instead of a third (f).

This kind of appoggiatura is handled less consistently by Bach. At times he writes it out, in full-sized or in small notes: Spitta gives examples of both. More often Bach omits any indication of it, and this leaves open the question of whether it is to be added. Spitta thinks the differentiation between Peter's first and second denials (No. 14, m. 15, and No. 18, m. 2) significant, and perhaps it is, though since the source for these passages is not in Bach's handwriting, one must beware of inferring too much. I do not believe Bach followed any thorough system in respect to this type of appoggiatura, and think there are many places where they may be added by the singer with good effect. It should be noted that Bach sometimes indicated them on unaccented syllables, and not always on strong beats. When they do occur on accented syllables, or on monosyllables, they inevitably give added emphasis to the word on which they occur, and I am inclined to decide the question principally on grounds of declamation. In general, if the appoggiatura would lend emphasis to a word which would have such emphasis in its place in the spoken sentence, I add it; otherwise not. The indications for such optional additions in this score thus take account of the different inflections of spoken German and spoken English.

An Arioso like No. 31 has qualities of both concerted music and recitative. And the "original" vocal part of this Arioso is, according to the BG editor, in Bach's handwriting. Several appoggiaturas are explicitly indicated by Bach in this number which in similar places in recitatives would presumably be "understood". But we must remember that the form in which we find them notated in BG (with the little slur-like mark instead of a small note) is not significant: it is merely the BG editor's way of identifying those appoggiaturas he found indicated in the manuscript *parts* as opposed to the score.

2. *Trills*

The one rule that seems to me generally applicable to Bach's trills is this:

The trill almost never begins with the notated tone, which is usually a consonant member of the harmony, *but almost always with its usually dissonant upper (or sometimes lower) neighbor.* Necessary exceptions to this rule are, I believe, rare; but since the St. John Passion contains one or two of them (No. 11, mm. 22–23), allowance must be made for them in formulating the rule.

The trills in this work fall, it seems to me, into two principal categories:
(1) *Prolonged, more or less expressive trills,* continuing through most or all of the duration of the note they ornament, and usually finished off with an "afterbeat" consisting of a two-note diatonic approach to the following tone (sometimes, but not usually, notated in full-size notes), or of a one-note anticipation of the following tone, usually notated as a full-size 8th or 16th after a dotted quarter or 8th bearing the trill; and

(2) *Short trills for the sake of added brilliance or accent,* taking up only an initial fraction of the time-value of the note they ornament, and coming to rest on that note, without "afterbeat".

Bach's own instructions concerning ornaments (in the *Clavierbüchlein vcr Wilhelm Friedemann Bach*) are too sparse to tell us much. They confirm what we know from every other source: that the trill begins on the dissonant appoggiatura rather than on the consonant principal tone. But they prove nothing about the rhythmic shape of the trill. François Couperin's *L'Art de Toucher le Clavecin* (1716-17) is more explicit on this point than most books:

Quoi que les tremblemens soient marqués egaux, dans la table des agrémens de mon premier livre, ils doivent cependant commencer plus lentement qu'ils finissent: mais, cette gradation doit être imperceptible. . . . Les tremblemens d'une valeur un peu considérable, renferment trois objets, qui dans l'execution ne paroissent qu'une même chose. 1°. L'appuy qui se doit former sur la note au dessus de l'essentièle. 2° Les batemens. 3° Le point d'arèst.

Although the trills are notated in equal notes, in the table of ornaments in my first book [of harpsichord pieces], they should nevertheless begin more slowly than they end: but this gradation must be imperceptible. . . . Trills of some duration comprise three elements: (1) The stress that is given to the note above the essential [i.e., notated] one; (2) the beats [i.e., the shake]; (3) the point of rest.

A l'égard des autres tremblemens ils sont arbitraires. . . .

As for the other trills, they are arbitrary. . . .

Couperin's instructions are for trills on the harpsichord, and we do not know specifically that Bach agreed with him. The exact shape of the trill has always varied from person to person and from case to case. But Couperin's remarks about the slow beginning, gradual increase of speed, and coming to rest of the trill (the latter before the afterbeat, and, it seems to me, more commonly before the one-note than before the two-note afterbeat) appear entirely appropriate to the prolonged, expressive trill in Bach, and I have been guided by them in many of the realizations suggested. Every editor confronted with the task of preparing a modern publication of music containing ornaments would like to dodge the responsibility of putting down in black and white his suggestions for their realization; or, if he cannot dodge it, would like to find a way of pointing out in connection with every one of them that the suggestions are approximate, tentative, and necessarily subject to the informed performer's taste and judgment.

* * *

What is the significance of ornament signs in the vocal parts of Bach's choruses? In Bach's own performances, we must remember, the "chorus" consisted of only three singers on a part. Perhaps all three sang the ornaments, guided by the "concertist" member of the trio; or perhaps he alone sang the ornaments and the "ripienists" disregarded them. With larger choruses the ornaments can be sung by all the singers in the slower movements. In fast movements, they must be at least simplified (e.g., by substituting an appoggiatura or a turn for a trill); and often they may be omitted without important loss.

C. HARMONIC (Figured basses and their realization)

Bach's period took for granted the presence in concerted music of a keyboard instrument to give harmonic support to the melodic instruments and voices. The keyboard parts, if elaborate and polyphonic in texture, were written out in full (or almost in full), and termed *obbligato:* such are the harpsichord parts of Bach's harpsichord-and-violin sonatas. More often, they were intended to supply a merely harmonic background. The parts were then written on one staff, in the bass clef, with figures to show—what?

Figured bass has for a long time been taught in schools as a branch of harmony: the bass line and figures are given, and the student is to work out a satisfactory four-part texture (approximating Bach's four-part chorale writing) above it, embodying the chords symbolized by the figures. Is this what Bach expected his organist to do, *ex tempore?*

It is not a task of surpassing difficulty: fluency in realizing a four-part texture at the keyboard from a fully figured bass is something that can be acquired, and undoubtedly the organist of Bach's time acquired it as part of his training. A letter of Emanuel Bach to Forkel tells us that J. S. Bach's pupils "had to begin their studies by learning pure four-part thorough bass. From this he went to chorales; first he added the basses to them himself, and they had to invent the alto and tenor. Then he taught them to devise the basses themselves. He particularly insisted on the writing out of the thorough bass in [four real] parts (*Aussetzen der Stimmen im Generalbasse*)." The significance of the figures and the details of their realization are treated in hundreds of 17th- and 18th-century books. It would seem that there could be little doubt about the nature of the keyboard accompaniment Bach must have wanted. Nevertheless, I believe this subject has been widely misunderstood since the revival of music of the continuo period.

The first misconception arose from the following descriptions of Bach's own figured-bass accompanying:

Whoever wishes to observe what delicacy in thorough bass and very good accompanying mean need only take the trouble to hear our Capellmeister Bach here, who accompanies every thorough bass to a solo so that one thinks it is a piece of concerted music and as if the melody he plays in the right hand were written beforehand.

—Lorenz Mizler, 1738

For the complete practical application of thorough bass it is necessary to know three species: (1) the simple or common; (2) the natural, or that which comes closest to the character of a melody or a piece; (3) the intricate or compound.

The excellent Bach possessed this third species in the highest degree; when he played, the upper voice [i.e., the written-out part for a melodic voice or instrument for which Bach was playing the accompaniment]* had to shine. By his exceedingly adroit accompaniment he gave it life when it had none. He knew how to imitate it so cleverly, with either the right hand or the left, and how to introduce an unexpected counter-theme against it, that the listener would have sworn that everything had been conscientiously written out. At the same time, the regular accompaniment was very little curtailed. In general his accompanying was always like a *concertante* part most conscientiously worked out and added as a companion to the upper voice so that at the appropriate time the upper voice would shine. This right was even given at times to the bass, without slighting the upper voice. Suffice it to say that anyone who missed hearing him missed a great deal.

—Johann Friedrich Daube, 1756

*Daube consistently uses the term *Oberstimme* in this sense, and the context makes it quite clear that this is what he means here.

He was also able, if a single bass part was laid before him (and often it was a poorly figured one) immediately to play from it a trio or quartet; nay, he even went so far, when he was in a cheerful humor and in the full consciousness of his powers, as to add extempore to three single parts a fourth part, and thus to make a quartet of a trio.

—Johann Nicolaus Forkel, 1802

These descriptions undoubtedly have considerable basis in truth, and they have offered a challenge which editors of Bach's works have been only too glad to accept: the challenge to concoct accompaniments as elaborate as the obbligato vocal or instrumental parts they were to go with. Editors of the 19th and 20th centuries gave themselves free rein in this respect, with results that have been pointed out by Terry. Of the unfigured bass to an aria in Cantata No. 3, the Breitkopf & Härtel vocal score contains the following realization:

But a surviving sheet of music paper bears the following fourteen measures in Bach's handwriting:

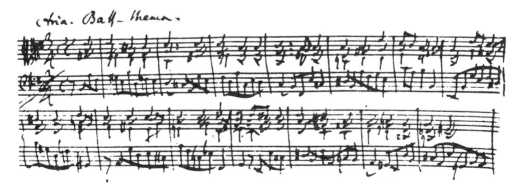

There are also extant realizations of figured basses by Bach pupils—by Gerber, with corrections by Bach, of an Albinoni violin sonata, and by Kirnberger, probably written after Bach's death, of the Trio Sonata in the *Musikalisches Opfer*. These realizations are in plain and sober four-part style. How does this testimony affect the notion that Bach wanted elaborate, polyphonic accompaniments?

One answer is, I think, that the elaborate style described by Mizler, Daube, and Forkel was something that Bach permitted himself in the performance of works by his contemporaries—works which were far less complex, less worked out than his own, and which left plentiful opportunities and often gaps for just such elaboration as he enjoyed devising for them. Forkel's description is doubtless based mainly on an earlier letter to him from Emanuel, in which the latter wrote:

> Thanks to his greatness in harmony, he accompanied trios on more than one occasion on the spur of the moment and, being in a good humor and knowing that the composer would not take it amiss, and on the basis of a sparsely figured continuo part just set before him, converted them into complete quartets, astounding the composer of the trios.

We have no reason to believe that when Bach played a keyboard accompaniment to his own obbligato parts he added anything elaborate. And even the elaborate accompaniments described were undoubtedly played mostly on the harpsichord—not on the organ—in secular chamber music.

No doubt when he played the accompaniment to one of his own chamber works, the listener would also "have sworn that everything had been conscientiously written out." But that may have been simply because the accompaniment was so perfectly pat—not because it was elaborate. The accompaniment to Schubert's *Haidenröslein* is written out, and it could not be improved upon, but it is not anything that could not have been improvised even by someone less spectacularly gifted than Bach. The same is true of the left-hand part of the *Adagio* movement of the early Organ Toccata in C major, which Max Schneider rightly points to as the kind of texture Bach doubtless would have supplied in a continuo accompaniment if the right-hand melody had been given to an obbligato instrument.*

As for the four-part chorale texture: we have plentiful written evidence that it was not clung to even on the harpsichord; and anyone who thinks it can be maintained with good results in accompanying on the organ has simply not tried it, or if he has tried it he has not listened to what it produced. It obscures melodic detail in the inner voices. And *above all it obtrudes a continuous volume of sound, as loud on the weakest part of the weakest beat as on the strongest of the strong.* This cannot be what any enlightened musician can ever have desired, irrespective of style or period. The continuous four-part style of figured-bass realization in concerted music, often possible on the harpsichord, where sustained tones quickly recede far into the background, is not possible on the organ.

---

*No. 60, accompanied only by 'cello and organ, invites the attempt at an accompaniment something like what Mizler and Forkel describe. But why did Bach write no obbligato instrumental parts for this aria? Doubtless because the parts he did write "had to shine", as Daube puts it. It seems to me that, tempting as it is to write a fully melodic right-hand part, the principal instrumental interest must be left to the 'cello, and not usurped by the organ.

Of course the "samples" of Bach's or his pupils' realizations of figured basses may mean anything. They may be models of what to do in a particular set of circumstances, or for a particular organist or harpsichordist, perhaps not very accomplished. They may be nothing but exercises for students. Gerber's realization contains awkwardnesses that prove that Bach did not revise it at all thoroughly. Bach taught his pupils the essentials of good voice-leading *through* four-part chorale harmonization and figured-bass realization. A knowledge of these essentials was and is a prerequisite to good continuo playing, something that every student must master on his way to artistic maturity. This point is too often forgotten in interpreting books of the period on thorough bass: they were mostly written for beginners, and their authors themselves were not always the most gifted or sensitive musicians. How much of the actual musical practice of our day will a scholar of 2150 A. D. be able to reconstruct from even our best books on harmony and counterpoint? At best, such books describe a normal practice; but Bach's works were anything but normal music.

As for the figures themselves, we must again look behind the appearance of the BG scores to see what they mean. But the BG scores are not always based on scores by Bach, as has been mentioned; sometimes they are based partly or wholly on "original" vocal and instrumental *parts*, which the BG editor reproduces as best he can in score. I say "as best he can" because he cannot reproduce all the variant, conflicting, and doubtful readings of duplicate parts in one score, and even in the critical account he gives of his sources there must always come a point at which editorial discretion calls a halt to the description of minutiae. Unfortunately, it is impossible for any editor to foresee all the different points of view from which works as important to musicians as those of Bach will be scrutinized; so too often we are left in doubt about a detail which seemed of no importance to the editor, but turns out to be of importance from a point of view he could not anticipate.

For example, the reader will look in vain through the BG descriptions of the sources for the St. John Passion and many other works of Bach containing important recitative portions for the answer to this question: What did the organist play from? Was it really a single bass-clef staff with figures, without either words or vocal line to help him follow the free, hardly metrical recitation of the Evangelist and the protagonists? One must hunt high and low through the works of Bach scholars before one can infer that it was. Spitta, Schering, and the BG editors mention a few instances in which the organ part includes a vocal line, and this implies clearly that in general the "original" organ part did consist of a single staff.* (This part for the St. John Passion was not among the BG editor's source material.) Thus it is clear that the horizontal space-intervals that separate figures occurring between bass notes rather than directly under them—that is, the metric position of such figures

---

*The implication is clear, but the facts may not be as implied. I have recently acquired a microfilm of the original parts of Cantata No. 88, in which the organ part for the recitative is written on two staves, one for the vocal line and one for the bass—which explains why, as BG XX says, "Bezifferung fehlt" (figuring is lacking). On the one autograph page of recitative from Bach's score of the St. John reproduced in facsimile in BG XLIV (containing the first eleven measures of No. 2) only one figured-bass symbol occurs—the one on the second beat of m. 5. Why? Probably because this is the one chord that would be least clearly implied by a part consisting only of the vocal and continuo lines. It would seem that Bach, when he wrote this page, had in mind the copyist who was to make the continuo part. Everything else would be clear to the organist, Bach could assume, from the two staves to be copied. But here the organist might easily play a triad or a $\frac{6}{5}$ chord if the symbol $\frac{6}{4\natural}$ were not provided for his guidance.

—has been determined by the editor, not by Bach or his copyist. (Bach rarely had occasion to write figures into his scores.) There are times when we need to know this: need to know that if we use our own judgment in re-spacing such figures—i.e., place chords at points in the measure slightly different from those indicated in BG—we are pitting our judgment against the editor's, and not necessarily against Bach's.

Anyone who has played or written out a good many realizations from the BG figured basses will have found many places where the figures come too thick and fast—not for convenience, but for an appropriate accompaniment. Sometimes there seems no good reason for the use of such figures, as in No. 60, m. 11, the second and third 8ths, where a dash would have indicated the same harmony more simply and clearly. Then we may remind ourselves that the BG figures for this work are mostly not taken from any autograph of Bach's, or even from any of the "original" material, but rather from that manuscript copy of the score made forty or fifty years later by Emanuel Bach's chorister Hering. Sometimes, as in many of the recitatives, they make perfectly good sense, but seem to provide for an unnecessarily detailed and fussy accompaniment.

In such passages we must realize that the organist, having only a single line before him, with figures, had to be able to follow the recitative singer closely: perhaps the figures served him as a sort of shorthand, not so much for what he was to play as for what was going on in the recitative, to which he must adapt his accompaniment. The first three measures of No. 14 provide an example:

Of course, on a harpsichord all these figures could be worked into the realization as indicated without disturbing the flow of the recitative; but on the organ they would be too "busy", it seems to me, even if the two a's (here written in long values) were played short. Emanuel Bach, in the second volume of his *Versuch* (1762, Ch. XXXVIII, § 6), suggests that in theater recitatives such details are often best omitted, even on the harpsichord. I think the figures in such cases are perhaps just as much an indication of what not to play, of what is already included in the written-out part or parts, as of what to play. Bach's notation became more explicit in many ways as he grew older. We have already seen how he notated the chords in the St. Matthew recitatives short, as he intended them to be played, while in earlier works he followed the conventional notation in long note-values. A study of the figures in the St.

Matthew recitatives will show how much more sparse they are, how much more freedom they give the narrator than those of the St. John, literally interpreted. Compare, for example, the opening measures of No. 39 of the St. Matthew

with the preceding example from the St. John. (I have inserted in brackets the figuring which would parallel that of the St. John, but which Bach did *not* write in the St. Matthew. How far Bach went in the St. Matthew in simplifying the accompaniment is strikingly illustrated in the opening measures of the Recitative No. 32, where the Evangelist, starting from a dominant of G major, modulates through a diminished-seventh chord into E minor without the slightest support from the continuo.)

Perhaps this is a change of style in recitative accompaniment; perhaps Bach learned over the years to strip away the unessentials. But equally likely, it seems to me, is the assumption that he simply became more explicit as he grew older, writing more and more carefully just what he wanted to have played. It still remains something of a mystery how the organist and 'cellist or bass violist could follow the recitative singers in all their free divagations from strict meter, guided only by such sparse figures as those in the St. Matthew; but that mystery fortunately does not have to be solved in commenting on the St. John.

We need not exclude the possibility that Bach conducted the recitatives, cumbersome as that procedure seems. Everyone at the Thomas-Kirche was inclined to stand very strictly on his prerogatives: it is doubtful that the Cantor would have condescended to replace the organist in accompanying, even if the organist had been willing to yield his bench to him. (The idea that the Rückpositiv—the portion of the organ used for accompaniment— was playable from a separate keyboard has been exploded.) Voigt (1742, in the book referred to earlier, p. 86) writes:

Was tutti und Arien anlangen, da lasse ich es gelten, wenn der Director die Violine in der Hand hat, und mit spielet, wenn er nur zum Anfange 1 bis 2 Tacte dirigiret, damit die Instrumentalisten und Vocalisten in eine richtige Mensur kommen: beym Recit. aber sollte billig der Tact gegeben werden.

As regards the tutti and the arias, I hold it to be appropriate, if the Director has a violin in his hand and plays along [with the orchestra] only one or two measures at the beginning, so that the instrumentalists and vocalists may find the right tempo; but in recitatives the beat should really be given.

Perhaps Voigt is thinking of recitatives accompanied by full strings, rather than of those with continuo only. And Schröter (p. 186) says recitatives should not be conducted.

Anyone who is disturbed by the fact that many of the figures in the recitatives are not reflected in the realizations in this edition can easily supply what is missing, since all the figures in the recitatives (and in No. 60) are reproduced exactly as in BG. In the concerted numbers I have reproduced the BG figures only in passages where the obbligato instruments drop out and the accompaniment is left entirely to the continuo. The figures under measures in which there are fully written out parts for the obbligato instruments tell us little that is not clear from the score without the figures.

D. EXPRESSIVE

Concerning nuances of dynamics and tempo variation, we are in the habit of saying that Bach's custom of including few expression marks leaves these matters mostly to the taste of the performer. This is only partly true: more can be read out of his notation than may at first appear. We have already seen this in the relationship of time-signatures to tempo. There is also something important to be read between the lines concerning variations of tempo.

I. Variations of Tempo

We know that it was customary in the 18th century to ornament cadences with freely improvised material, samples of which are generously supplied by the books of the period. We may be fairly sure that in this respect, as in others, Bach expected less than most composers in the way of improvisatory addition from his singers. The instructions for elaborating cadences describe a practice that belonged to the virtuosi of the period: above all, the opera-singers, but also instrumental virtuosi, who imitated their vocal colleagues in this respect. Bach wrote out some instrumental cadenzas, perhaps as notations of his own improvisations of this type. (See, for example, those in the harpsichord concertos, contained in BG Jahrg. XVII.) But his vocal music was mostly written not for opera-singers but for the men and boys of the Leipzig choirs, who were not virtuosi, and from whom he clearly did not expect (and probably would not have tolerated) anything very substantial in the way of improvisatory additions. He did undoubtedly, however, expect some trills that he did not explicitly call for; and he clearly expected them to approach the cadence with more rhythmic freedom and leisure than they could afford in the regular course of the music. The proof is that more often than not, in his arias, whatever obbligato instruments are employed drop out a measure or two before the cadence, and leave the voice accompanied only by the continuo instruments. The continuo players were accustomed to following the more or less free rhythms of the voices in recitatives, and with the limited rehearsal time Bach had at his disposal it was practical to avoid the difficulties of working out the rhythmically freer parts of the arias with the singer and obbligato instruments together by simply dropping the latter.

Great artists invariably make a virtue of necessity, and the form of Bach's arias, with the instrumental ritornelli entering immediately after the cadence, capitalizes on what probably originated as a purely practical procedure.

Thus we do not need the rather scattered references to retards at cadences that occur in the writings of the period to realize that Bach frequently intended them, although he never used the markings *"rall."* or *"rit."* It would be a mistake however, to adopt a literal interpretation of this practice, and limit cadential retards to those passages accompanied by continuo only. Bach was a practical musician, but he was not only practical: sometimes musical considerations of a higher order call for the collaboration of the obbligato instruments throughout a piece, or in some cadences and not in others. The question of the placing of retards, and of their degree and shape, cannot be shifted from the domain of taste and instinct to that of quorum-counting. Nor is every instance of the dropping out of the obbligato parts an invitation to singers to bring the rhythmic flow of a piece to a standstill. But it is a reminder, especially to singers who have been taught that Bach is unremittingly severe, that some of their musical instincts are not as wrong as pedantic teachers would have them believe.

Bach uses the word *Adagio* in the St. John Passion not only at the beginning of movements, but also in the course of recitatives: in passages of more or less arioso character for expressive reasons (e.g., end of No. 18), or in passages of special solemnity, such as the wording of the sign Pilate places on the Cross (No. 49) or the quotations the Evangelist adduces from the Old Testament to show the fulfillment of ancient prophecies (Nos. 55, 64). In all these cases it refers more to the change in the character of the singing than to any specific tempo such as it may suggest to modern musicians. The freely reciting character of the recitatives is interrupted, and the Evangelist adopts a more solemn and measured style, but not necessarily a very slow tempo.

It has been mentioned in connection with the determination of tempi that two factors importantly affecting the choice to be made are (1) the denomination of the shortest notes, and (2) the mood of the piece. Both of these factors, I think, argue in favor of implications that No. 44 begins somewhat faster than No. 36, and settles down to the tempo of the earlier piece after three measures; and that in No. 48, measure 106 should be marked (for the modern musician) *poco meno mosso* and measure 117 *a tempo*. Measure 174 in this same number surely needs the emphasis and finality that Bach would have indicated by marking it *Adagio* (i.e., about twice as slow as the prevailing tempo), with the *a tempo* coming on the succeeding measure.

2. *Dynamics*

Concerning dynamics, too, Bach's markings tell us somewhat more than would at first appear. We must remember, first of all, that the instruments of his day did not have as wide a range of dynamics as ours: in general their loudest was nowhere near as loud as ours, and the difference between their loudest and softest was not as great. Thus by the mere number and type of instruments he chose for each piece he gave a fairly definite idea of the dynamics he intended. He drew certain stops, so to speak, and this "registration" establishes the general dynamic level for the piece. Within a single movement, he does use directions like *piano*, *pianissimo*, and *forte*, but these, of course, need to be read in the light of the instrumentation. In order to give the reader as accurate a picture as possible of the markings given in BG, they are reproduced exactly in this edition, any modifications that seem necessary for the player of the keyboard reduction being given in brackets.

Only two of all the movements in the St. John Passion have dynamic markings at the beginning: No. 31, the *pianissimo* in the continuo, and No. 62, the *piano* in the flutes and oboes.   But every aria except No. 32 contains the marking *piano* (in No. 48, *pianissimo*) at the point where the voice enters, after the instrumental introduction.   This must mean that the introductions are all thought of as being louder than *piano*.   In fact, this is what it does mean, as we see from the fact that when the voice drops out again the instrumental parts are regularly marked *forte*.

Bach clearly assumes that every instrumental introduction not otherwise marked begins in a good, healthy tone representing the *forte* of the instruments and voices participating.*   This does not mean, of course, that all instruments are to play equally loud.   It means that the general impression is to be *forte*, and that he conveyed the dynamic proportions to the individual players by the sign-language of the conductor, as well as orally, instead of marking different instruments with different dynamics, as the modern composer does.

From the time of Bach to the present day there has been an almost steady increase in the explicitness with which composers mark the dynamics and other expressive features for each individual instrument.   Along with this development has come an increasing tendency to look on dynamic markings as quasi-absolute indications of volume of sound.   The orchestral writing of Stravinsky marks the furthest development in this direction, approaching the extreme in which the instrumentalist hardly has to have mastered anything but the technique of his instrument.   If he takes the beat from the conductor, and follows all the markings of dynamics and articulation in his part, he hardly needs to be able to hear a note: the effect of the total has been planned in all its details by the architect, and he need only slip his bricks of predetermined size, shape, and color into their predetermined places. Bach's time expected both more and less of its performers: less in some aspects of technique, and far more in the matter of listening to each other and being guided by what they heard.

As for the effects of *crescendo* and *diminuendo*, much of Bach's music was planned, and sounds best, without any such gradual changes.   On the harpsichord and organ, Bach frequently provided for gradual increases and decreases of volume when he wanted them, by increasing and decreasing the number of tones to be played simultaneously.   On the harpsichord, which had no pedals in his day, there was little else he could do; on the organ, there was nothing.   On both instruments he could draw additional stops, or cancel them, whenever he had one hand free; but this would provide at best only an increase or decrease by definite steps.

Voices and wind and string instruments, on the other hand, have always been subject to gradual changes of volume and color, and have unquestionably always been used to produce such changes, though the instruments were not capable of as wide variations in Bach's day as they are in ours. The ear of an imaginative listener quickly accepts the inability of the harpsichord and

---

*Even in the Italian Concerto, published by Bach with dynamic markings as explicit as any he ever provided, the unquestionably *forte* opening is not so marked.   And note that after the marking *piano* for the parentheses in the recitatives Nos. 64 and 66, even they are marked *forte*.   Telemann, in the foreword to his *Harmonischer Gottesdienst* says explicitly that "the beginning of every piece [in his collection] belongs to the *forte*, where *piano* is not expressly marked."

organ to make the kind of gradual changes possible to instruments on which the players more directly control the tone. It resents too obvious attempts on the part of players with modern devices at their disposal to imitate effects essentially foreign to their instrument. Harpsichord and organ music is accepted by the ear as an abstraction; clumsy attempts to conceal its abstract quality only draw attention to the impossibility of doing so. (I say "clumsy attempts", because on both the organ and the harpsichord skilful modern performers succeed in very subtle manipulation of their resources to achieve a result which is in no way obtrusive.) In the same way, the ear quickly hears that a voice or a violin is not made for such abstractions, that its volume and color are constantly changing. Accordingly, the ear demands that such changes should be purposeful and controlled.

Bach often plans dynamic effects simply by his choice of the register in which a voice or instrument is to perform certain material. But his ideas do not always lend themselves to such planning, and his plans are frequently upset by our performing his music with instruments and voices different from those he wrote for. So in the performance of his music there is no substitute for the ever-alert ear of every performer.

Dynamic indications in this edition have been held to a minimum; they include all of the markings in BG and a few supplementary ones added in brackets by me. In the latter I have tried for the most part only to carry out Bach's implicit scheme. Occasionally, as in Nos. 38 and 42, I have offered suggestions for a purely optional scheme not clearly implied by Bach, but suggested to me by the texture, expression, and structure of the music, over years of familiarity with the performance problems of these pieces.

3. *Phrasing and Articulation*

Bach used in this work only two types of marking for phrasing and articulation: slurs and dots. ("Spiccato" in his time meant simply "detached"—i.e., not slurred.) In his vigorous handwriting, dots sometimes look like vertical dashes, or even horizontal ones, but he does not seem to have intended any differentiation of this sort. His markings are usually more explicit in the original parts than in the scores—naturally: the parts were for the players' use, and the scores mostly for his own.

Why are slurs and dots so plentiful in Bach's string and wind parts, much less plentiful in his keyboard music, and sparse in his vocal parts? The answer in regard to vocal music is that the words constitute far more explicit "markings" than slurs or dots, in most cases.

As to the differences between the keyboard music on the one hand and the string and wind parts on the other, there are several explanations. First of all, keyboard players (in Bach's day they played all keyboard instruments, including the organ) were expected to possess broader and more thorough musicianship than other instrumentalists, who were looked upon as closer to the artisan class. Keyboard players were expected to have mastered thorough bass. They had to know the meaning and execution of many signs for ornaments which were either written out in full or omitted altogether for other instruments. Similarly, more knowledge and taste could be expected of keyboard players in deciding questions of articulation and phrasing.

Secondly, slurs mean different things to players of different instruments, and precision in their use in keyboard music is much younger than in works for string and woodwind instruments. Changes of bow (i.e., of direction of bow-stroke) are an elementary necessity on string instruments, and the use of the slur or similar indications to show how many notes are to be played on one bow is much older than Bach. Tonguing on wind instruments (i.e., the definite attack at the beginning of a note or group of notes accomplished by the tongue, as if pronouncing the consonants *t* or *d*) is almost as elementary, and the slur shows how many notes are to be played without such separation.

The effect of the slur on phrasing and articulation is similar in string and wind playing: the first note under the slur, being the first note of the new bow or the only tongued note of the slurred group, naturally receives a certain accentuation by virtue of the articulation alone, *other things being equal.* Of course there are all varieties of tonguing, from gentle to explosive, and all kinds of subtlety in managing the bow's change of direction, which may make other things anything but equal.

But on keyboard instruments the slur simply means *legato:* every note is tongued, so to speak, but each note under a slur is sustained until the next note enters. A violinist or an oboist playing a steady series of sixteenth-notes in a $\frac{4}{4}$ measure can bow them or tongue them so that the slurs group them by quarters, as do the beams that connect their stems, without any real interruption of the *legato* between beats; yet the first of each group of four sixteenths receives just that slight differentiation that is its due. No. 1 of the St. John Passion is full of such slurring.

But to transfer such slurs to keyboard notation makes no sense except to the reader who constantly remembers that they are borrowed from music for other instruments. The only technical meaning such slurring could have for a keyboard player would be a legato interrupted before every beat, which would make musical nonsense. It is true that Mozart, Beethoven, and many other great composers frequently did not hesitate to take over such slurring from the other instruments into their keyboard works. But in a period as interested as ours is in the letter of the composer's original text, it would be misleading to include in a keyboard reduction slurs that have meaning only for the instrumental parts in which they occur. *For this reason, the slurs in this edition do not correspond literally with those in BG, except where a literal interpretation of them at the keyboard will result in an articulation similar to that intended for the instrument represented.*

Several other reservations must be made about Bach's slurring. For one thing, considerable discretion needs to be used at times to decide (when possible on the basis of parallel passages) just how many notes his slurs are intended to include. Even in those movements for which the BG editor had material in Bach's handwriting as a source, there is often room for doubt, as a glance at Jahrg. XLIV of BG will show. But in preparing the work for engraving, the BG editor had to resolve his doubts and make choices which may not always reflect Bach's intentions. Frequently, without doubt, he included slurs consistently throughout a movement which Bach had marked only here and there. For frequently Bach marked only one passage explicity, probably implying that similar passages were to be performed in similar manner.

Sometimes, however, the BG editor did not complete the consistent marking of a movement. For example, the first two notes in the bass of No. 13 are slurred in BG, but no other eighth-notes in the bass are slurred anywhere in this movement. This leaves us free to speculate whether Bach intended most or all of these two-note figures in the bass to be slurred. My own choice is to believe that the solitary slur at the beginning of the aria results from a mistake on the part of the BG editor or of Bach's copyist, or possibly from a slip of the pen or an accidental ink mark by Bach himself, and that these eighth-notes in the bass represent the "footsteps" referred to in the first line of the text, which are better symbolized by detached eighths than by slurred ones.

Dots can have many meanings too, from the sharpest staccato to the gentlest interruption of the legato, or even the mere pulsations of the *Bebung* effect on the clavichord and similar effects on other instruments. But where dots are concerned there is no such contradiction between the notations for keyboard (except clavichord, with which we are not concerned here) and for other instruments. *Accordingly, the dots in this edition reproduce literally those in BG.*

V. Translating the Text

No one should imagine that the best singing translation can ever take the place of the original text. No matter how poor the original may be—and the texts of Bach's non-Scriptural movements are often very poor indeed—there is one respect in which no translation can ever approach them: the composer wrote his music to fit them. One of the superiorities of the human voice over all other instruments consists in the infinite nuances of articulation possible to it through words. No violinist's bow, no pianist's fingers, no woodwind player's tongue can rival the word-pronouncing mechanisms in this respect. What wouldn't we give for completely explicit bowing and tonguing indications in Bach's instrumental works? Yet for his vocal music we have indications far more explicit than all the slurs, dots, dashes, fingerings, accent-marks, and other paraphernalia for indicating phrasing and articulation: indications that even show us the emotional coloring of individual tones. This is a strong argument for singing these works in the original language.

On the other hand, vocal music is meant to convey simultaneously musical and extra-musical meanings. The Passion is not just a musical composition. It is a religious music-drama, in which the music is calculated to intensify the impact of the words. And what impact can they have if they are sung in a language foreign to the listener—sometimes perhaps even to the singer?

There is no perfect resolving of these diametrically opposed and all-important considerations. The second one is usually considered paramount, and the Passion is usually sung in the language of the country where the performance takes place; but it would be foolish to shut one's eyes to the fact that either choice involves a great sacrifice. When the Passion is sung as part of a church service, it usually has to be done in the vernacular, whatever the artistic sacrifices involved. When it is sung in concert performance, the choice is not so clear.

Bach's congregation regularly had the texts of his choral works before them, in the form of booklets specially printed for this purpose—like libretti in the opera house, except that presumably the church was light enough to enable them to follow the texts while the music was being sung. (From this we can infer that then as now not all singers enunciated with perfect clarity and the acoustics varied from one part of a church to another. The churches were not small, and the singers, placed as they were in choir-lofts above and behind the congregation, could not be seen while they sang.) My own preference is for a similar solution today: sing the original text, making sure that all the singers know exactly what they are singing, and let the congregation or audience follow the text in copies provided them for the purpose, complete in both languages.*

As for the considerations that must guide the translator, I cannot resist quoting a paragraph from Tovey's essay on Haydn's *Creation*, written as a program note for Tovey's own performance of the work in Edinburgh, for which he had edited the text:

> If you want to preserve Haydn's or Bach's exact notes in their recitatives you must sing them in German. Bach and Handel were ready enough to sacrifice originally good declamation in transcribing formal music to new texts; but they never** transcribed a recitative to a new text. It was infinitely less trouble to compose a new recitative. And recitative that does not fall into the speech rhythm of the language in which it is sung is neither speech nor language nor music. I shall doubtless be severely dealt with for altering the notes of Haydn's music; but, unlike the old Scotch lady who enjoyed sermons but "wudna hae the presoomption to understand them", I presume to understand Haydn's recitatives. I claim to take no liberties; once alterations are admitted, notes may be altered in a wrong way as well as in a right way; but the modern proposition that recitative-formulas must not be altered at all in translations is no more scholarly than translating "qu'est-ce que c'est que ça" by "what is this that this is that that".

Actually, Bach had no hesitation in changing even his "formal music" to fit new texts. We have an example of this very procedure in Nos. 38 and 42 of this work. But, of course, it was his own music he was changing. There is no question that as little should be changed by us as possible, and the slight changes in the recitatives in this edition to fit the English text are hardly worth mentioning, particularly since the original is given throughout.

In preparing the English translation of this work, I have had the great advantage of being able to draw freely on the previous work of two skilled and conscientious translators, Henry S. Drinker and the late Harvey Officer. Harvey Officer made a translation for the program notes of a performance in German conducted by Paul Boepple a dozen years ago, and he and I subsequently reworked it. Mr. Drinker, whose translations of all the Bach texts (and many others) sustain a level of quality far above that of any previously printed translations, was good enough to invite me to help myself to whatever I wanted from his version, and I took full advantage of his generosity. For the result I must take full responsibility, since I chose where to borrow and where to invent, but of whatever credit accrues I must pass the lion's share to the Drinker and Officer versions.

July 28, 1950   ARTHUR MENDEL

---

*Permission to print the texts should be applied for by writing to G. Schirmer, Inc., 609 Fifth Avenue, New York.

**"Never" is a big word, even when Tovey uses it. Actually, in one or two pairs of cantatas, Bach did use the same recitatives with different texts, making very minor adjustments here and there, but not quite everywhere they were needed. Doubtless he counted on the singer to give the words a somewhat more natural flow than a literal reading of his notation would produce.

BIBLIOGRAPHICAL NOTES

Scores

J. S. BACH, *Werke, herausgegeben von der Bach-Gesellschaft, Jahrg.* XII[1], Leipzig, 1863. (Ed. Wilhelm Rust.) Reprinted by J. W. Edwards, Ann Arbor, 1947.

_____ *Grosse Passionsmusik nach dem Evangelium Johannis,* J. Trautwein, Berlin, 1831. This is the first published edition of the score and contains some readings different from those in BG, as for example in No. 54 (see pp. 238 ff) and in No. 58 ("Vivace" instead of "Alla breve").

_____ *Passion nach dem Evangelisten Johannes,* Eulenburg, Leipzig-Vienna, n. d. Edited with an Introduction by Arnold Schering, dated 1925; based on BG and the original manuscripts.

Books and Magazines

(The numbers in the left-hand column refer to the earliest page of the Introduction on which information occurs drawn from among the following works.)

ii. PHILIPP SPITTA, *Johann Sebastian Bach,* Leipzig, 1873-1880, II, 348-367 and 811-815; English translation by Clara Bell and J. A. Fuller-Maitland, London, 1884, II, 519-537 and 709-712. After both the German and the English editions had appeared, Spitta published further material on the Aria No. 19 in the article *Die Arie "Ach, mein Sinn" aus der Johannes-Passion,* which appeared in the *Vierteljahrsschrift für Musikwissenschaft,* IV, 471, and later in his collected *Musikgeschichtliche Aufsätze,* Berlin, 1894, pp. 101-110.

iii. JOHANN GOTTFRIED WALTHER, *Musicalisches Lexicon,* Leipzig, 1732, p. 220.

iv. BERNHARD FRIEDRICH RICHTER, *Die Wahl Joh. Seb. Bachs zum Kantor der Thomasschule im Jahre 1723,* in *Bach-Jahrbuch,* 1905. *Zur Geschichte der Passionsaufführungen in Leipzig,* in *Bach-Jahrbuch,* 1911.

iv. The structure of the work in a different sense (allegedly symmetrical layout) is discussed by FRIEDRICH SMEND in his article *Die Johannes-Passion von Bach, auf ihren Bau untersucht,* in *Bach-Jahrbuch,* 1926.

v. SPITTA (German), II, 74-79.

HANS T. DAVID and ARTHUR MENDEL, Editors, *The Bach Reader,* New York, 1945, pp. 120-124.

vi. ARNOLD SCHERING, *J. S. Bachs Leipziger Kirchenmusik,* Leipzig, 1936. Schering somewhat overstates the case for the organ and against the harpsichord, and some of his arguments are faulty; nevertheless, the weight of the evidence he presents is overwhelmingly in favor of the organ as the regular continuo instrument in Bach's church music. His book contains valuable material **on** almost every subject discussed in this Introduction. It is at times somewhat dogmatic, but it is fully documented, so that one can usually tell what Schering bases his opinions on.

vii. On the registration of organ continuo parts, see also J. F. Petri, *Anleitung zur praktischen Musik*, Lauban, 1767, p. 42; Dom Bedos de Celles, *L'Art du Facteur d'Orgues*, 1766-77, p. 533 (IIIe Partie); C. G. Schröter, *Deutliche Anweisung zum Generalbass*, Halberstadt, 1772, pp. 185-190; J. J. Adlung, *Musica Mechanica Organoedi*, 1768, pp. 171, 184; *Ibid.*, *Anleitung zur musicalischen Gelahrtheit*, 1783, p. 586.

viii. Charles Sanford Terry, *Bach's Orchestra*, though not always accurate, contains a good deal of information on the instruments, many useful tables, and a rich bibliography.

On the solo-tutti question, see Arnold Schering, *Die Besetzung Bachscher Chöre*, in *Bach-Jahrbuch*, 1920.

ix. For detailed suggestions concerning performance of the St. John Passion with "symphonic" forces see Walter Reinhart, *Die Aufführung der Johannes-Passion von J. S. Bach und deren Probleme*, Leipzig, 1933.

ix. The dimensions of the Thomas-Kirche are given in *Beschreibende Darstellung der älteren Bau und Kunstdenkmäler des Königreichs Sachsen*, Dresden, 1896, XVIII & XXI.

ix. On the relations between meter and tempo in the mensural system, see Willi Apel, *The Notation of Polyphonic Music, 900-1600*, Fourth Edition, Cambridge, Massachusetts, 1949, pp. 188-195. On this question in Beethoven, see Rudolf Kolisch, *Tempo and Character in Beethoven's Music*, in *The Musical Quarterly*, April and July, 1943.

x. Johann Joachim Quantz, *Versuch einer Anweisung die Flöte traversiere zu spielen*, Berlin, 1752, XVII, vii, §§ 47-50, pp. 261-263. Franchinus Gafurius, *Practica Musicae*, 1496, III, 4, quoted in Georg Schünemann, *Geschichte des Dirigierens*, Leipzig, 1913, in which tempo questions are discussed at length.

xii. Albert Schweitzer, *J. S. Bach*, 2. Auflage, Leipzig, 1915, p. 353. Schweitzer discusses many of the questions here considered, but I have thought it better not to cite his remarks in most instances because, while often penetrating, they are so subjective and so little documented as to be dangerous material in the hands of those who cannot tell where his suggestions are based on 18th-century sources and where they voice only his personal opinions or those of his time (his book first appeared in 1905).

xv. Quantz, V, § 22, p. 59.

F. W. Marpurg, *Anleitung zum Clavierspielen*, Berlin, 1755, p. 24. This passage is translated in Ralph Kirkpatrick's edition of Bach's "*Goldberg*" *Variations*, New York, 1938.

CARL PHILIPP EMANUEL BACH, *Versuch über die wahre Art das Clavier zu spielen*, Berlin, 1752, I, iii, § 27, p. 114; English translation (*Essay on the True Art of Playing Keyboard Instruments*) by William J. Mitchell, New York, 1949, p. 160. In the latter, the translation of the word *Nachschlag* as "unaccented appoggiatura" is, I believe, erroneous; *Nachschlag* (literally: "after-stroke") seems to me to refer to the fact that the one note would have to be "struck after" the other one.

xvi. C. P. E. BACH, II, xxxviii, § 5, p. 316; English, p. 422.

QUANTZ, XVII, vi, § 30, pp. 236-237.

LEOPOLD MOZART, *Versuch einer gründlichen Violinschule*, Augsburg, 1756 (reprinted in facsimile, Vienna, 1922), XII, § 19, p. 262; English translation by Editha Knocker, London, 1948, p. 223.

C. P. E. BACH, I, iii, § 22; English, p. 157.

The question of *legato vs. staccato* on the organ in Bach's time is discussed in SPITTA, German, II, 132-133; English, II, 301. Many of the questions of performance of Bach's choral works are treated in this section of Spitta's book with more understanding and knowledge than is to be found in any other source.

xvii. SCHRÖTER, p. 185.

xviii. Cf. the facsimile reproductions of Caccini's *Nuove Musiche* (1601) and Monteverdi's *Orfeo* (1607).

xx. On the question of prolonging the notes bearing fermatas, I have found explicit references only long before Bach (SCHÜTZ), and long after him (PETRI, 1767, p. 110, and D. G. TÜRK, *Von den wichtigsten Pflichten eines Organisten*, Halle, 1787, p. 17 etc.).

xxi. J. A. SCHEIBE, *Critischer Musikus*, Hamburg, 1738, pp. 62-63, and J. A. BIRNBAUM, *Unpartheyische Anmerckungen* . . . , in MIZLER'S *Neu eröffnete Musicalische Bibliothek*, Leipzig, April, 1738, I, Part IV, 62-73. Translated in DAVID-MENDEL, *Bach Reader*, 237-252.

xxi ff. The most explicit descriptions of ornaments we have by 18th-century German writers are those of C. P. E. BACH, QUANTZ, and the German translation of PIETRO FRANCESCO TOSI, *Opinioni de' Cantori*, Bologna, 1723, by JOHANN FRIEDRICH AGRICOLA, under the title *Anleitung zur Singkunst*, Berlin, 1757. The extent to which they apply to J. S. Bach's music, however, is debatable, and varies from instance to instance.

xxii. Bach's own table of ornaments is reproduced in many books, more often than not inaccurately. It is given in facsimile in KIRKPATRICK's edition of the "*Goldberg*" *Variations*.

The appoggiaturas in Bach's Passions and Christmas Oratorio are discussed in detail in ARNOLD SCHERING, *Vorhalte und Vorschläge in Bachs Passionen*, in *Bach-Jahrbuch*, 1923. Schering's historical knowledge of Bach's Leipzig period was unmatched, but in specifically musical matters his opinion carries little weight, since he was apparently not fully at home in the domains of practical music-making or artistic perception.

xxviii ff. *Bach Reader*, pp. 279, 231, 256, 311; full bibliographical information there.

xxix ff. TERRY, *Bach's Orchestra*, p. 170. The Gerber continuo is given in SPITTA (German, II, following p. 214; English, III, 388-398); the Kirnberger in HANS T. DAVID's edition of Bach's *Musical Offering*, New York, 1944. David's book, *Bach's Musical Offering*, New York, 1945, also contains much helpful material on performance.

xxx. *Bach Reader*, p. 277.

MAX SCHNEIDER, *Der Generalbass J. S. Bachs*, in *Jahrbuch der Musikbibliothek Peters*, 1914-1915, pp. 27-42.

xxxi. SPITTA, German, II, 124, 772; English, II, 292, 677.

J. C. VOIGT, *Gespräch von der Musik*, Erfurt, 1742, says no composer will give himself the trouble of copying out vocal parts above the continuo line, or even the figures except in a difficult recitative; but of course all Bach's recitatives are "difficult" compared to the average in his time. WALTHER (under *Recitativo*) says it is necessary that the vocal line of the recitative should be copied above the bass, so that the accompanist can allow the singer the necessary freedom. An example of a Bach continuo so notated is given in SCHERING, p. 75.

xxxiii. VOIGT recommends that the Cantor should conduct the recitatives, and perhaps that is how they were managed in the St. Matthew, and even in the St. John. Even today, when the orchestra and organ parts contain the vocal line, that seems to be the best solution.

xxxiv. Instructions for improvising cadenzas are given by QUANTZ, C. P. E. BACH, AGRICOLA, and others. Examples of cadenzas written out in Bach's works may be found in BG XVII (the harpsichord concertos).

CONTENTS OF MUSIC

PART I

PART II

The Passion according to St. John

Translation adapted by A.M.
from King James version and
translations by Henry S. Drinker
and Harvey Officer

Johann Sebastian Bach
Edited by Arthur Mendel

Part I
No.1. Chorus

*Small notes are used for various purposes in this edition: in some of the choruses, as in this one, simply as a device to keep the different types of material used in the accompaniment clear.

[No.1]

[No. 1]

[No.1]

* Throughout this edition, expression marks not in brackets are those included in BG, from the
original manuscripts. See pp. xxxv ff. and 237 ff.

[No. 1]

No. 2. Recitative

* In all the recitatives, the lower staff of the accompaniment and the figures reproduce exactly and completely the original continuo parts as reproduced in BG, except for an occasional octave transposition. The right-hand part is, of course, the present editor's reconstruction of what the improvised organ accompaniment may have been like. See pp. xxviii ff.

**Bracketed slurs above the staff indicate the possibility of substituting an upper appoggiatura for the first of the two identical tones: Where this possibility applies to one language only, the upper slur (⌒) is used for the German and the lower slur (‿) for the English. See pp. xxiii ff.

Ke-dron
Ce-dron

riet,   wuss-te den Ort auch,   denn Je-sus ver-sam-mel-te sich oft   da-selbst mit
trayed him, knew the place full well;   for Je-sus had of-ten wait-ed there   to meet with

sei-nen Jün-gern;   da nun Ju-das zu sich hat-te ge-nom-men die
his dis-ci-ples.   Now then, Ju-das, hav-ing gath-ered a bod-y of

Schar,   und der Ho-hen-prie-ster und Pha-ri-sä-er Die-ner, kommt er da-
men   whom the chief priests and the Pha-ri-sees had sent him, now com-eth

12

hin mit Fack-eln, Lamp-en, und mit Waf-fen. Als nun
forth with torch-es, lan-terns, and with weap-ons. There-fore

14

Je-sus wuss-te Al-les, was ihm be-geg-nen soll-te, ging er hin-
Je-sus, know-ing all things that were to come up-on him, went straight-way

16

Jesus   Evangelist

aus und sprach zu ih-nen: Wen su-chet ihr? Sie ant-wor-te-ten
forth and said to them: Whom seek ye here? And they an - swered

*Page numbers in brackets refer each solo singer to his next appearance.

No. 3. Chorus

*Concerning the instrumentation of the bass line throughout this **work, see p. viii.**

No. 4. Recitative

*In numbering, incomplete measures at the beginnings of recitatives are not counted.

42262

No. 5. Chorus

No. 6. Recitative

No. 7. Chorale

O gro - sse Lieb', o Lieb' ohn' al - le Ma - sse, die
O won - drous Love, o Love all love ex - cel - ling, Which

dich ge-bracht auf die - se Mar - ter-stra - sse, ich leb - te mit der
bade Thee make this vale of tears Thy dwell - ing, I live on earth and

Continuo

Welt in Lust__ und__ Freu - den, und du musst lei - den.
earth - ly plea - sures__ cher - ish, And Thou must per - ish.

*On the significance of the fermatas, see pp. xx f.

No. 8. Recitative

Evangelist

Auf dass das Wort er - fül - let wür - de, wel - ches er sag - te: Ich
So that the word might be ful - filled which he had spo - ken: I

ha - be der Kei - ne ver - lo - ren, die du mir ge - ge - ben hast.
have not lost one dis - ci - ple of them which thou gav - est me.

Da hat - te Si - mon Pe - trus ein Schwert, und zog es aus,
Then Si - mon Pe - ter, hav - ing a sword, he drew it forth,

und schlug nach des Ho - hen - prie - sters Knecht, und hieb ihm sein recht'
and struck at the high priest's serv - ing man, and cut the man's right

No. 9. Chorale

Dein Will' ge - scheh', Herr Gott, zu - gleich auf Er - den wie im
Thy will, O__ Lord__ our God, be done On earth as round Thy

Him - mel - reich; gieb uns Ge - duld in Lei - dens - zeit, Ge -
heav'n-ly__ throne. Thy pa - tience, Lord, on us be - stow, That

hor - sam - sein in__ Lieb' und Leid, wehr' und__ steur' al - lem
we o - bey in__ weal and woe. Stay Thou__ the hand and

Fleisch und Blut, das wi - der dei - nen Wil - len tut.
spoil the skill Of them that work a - gainst Thy will.

No. 10. Recitative

7

prie-ster war; es war a-ber Ca - i - phas, der den Ju - den
high priest. Now 'twas this same Ca - ia - phas who had told the

9

riet, es wä - re gut, dass ein Mensch wür-de um-bracht für das Volk.
Jews it would be well that one man should per - ish for them all. [p.41]

7♭
5

6

6♭

5
♯

No. 11. Aria

Alto

[♩ = 60 - 72; see pp. ix ff.] Ob. I

[mf] Ob. II

6

Von den ___ Stri -
From the ___ tan - gle ___

[3/2] tr

** piano

tr
*

7

* Or the C♯ may be left untrilled, care then being taken to play the F with the C♯, *on* the second beat.

Small notes in accompaniments to the arias (and No. 67) indicate harmonic filling of the type supplied, in a performance with orchestra, by the organ; here added by the present editor. See **pp. xxviii ff.

ckenmei-ner Sün - den ___ mich zu ent-bin - den,mich zu ent-bin -
of my trans-gres - sions, ___ but to un-bind ___ me,but to un-bind ___

- den,wird mein Heil ge - bun - den.
___ me is my dear - est Sav - iour bound.

Von den Stri - cken
From the tan - gle

mei - ner ___ Sün - den mich zu ent-bin - den,mich zu ent-bin -
of ___ my trans-gres - sions,but to un-bind ___ me, but to un-bind ___

(One of the rare situations in which a Bach trill may best
begin on the notated tone, rather than on its upper neighbor,because
of the consecutive octaves with the bass which the latter would cause.)

*According to BG, the manuscripts seem to disagree, some containing
the rhythm here given and some (doubtless by error) having:

No. 12. Recitative

Evangelist

Si-mon Pe-trus a-ber fol - ge - te Je-su nach, und ein an-d'rer Jün-ger.
Si-mon Pe-ter al-so fol-lowed in Je-sus' path, and an-oth-er dis-ci-ple. [p.49]

* In BG, only one flat is in the signature, the E♭ being added as an accidental.

No. 13. Aria
Soprano

Ich fol - ge dir gleich-falls mit
I fol - low Thee al - so with

freu-di - gen Schritten,
joy-light-ened foot-steps,

ich
I

* On the question of whether these two notes, and similar figures in this number, should be slurred, see p. **xxxix**.

In passages here marked *sempre legato*, BG has a slur for each full measure. See pp. **xxxvii ff.

[No. 13]

[No. 13]

Schrit - ten, und las - se_ dich nicht, mein Le - ben, mein
foot-steps, Nor stray from thy sight, My life and my

Licht, ich fol - - - - - -
light, I fol - - - - - -

- - ge_ dir gleich-falls mit freu-di - gen Schrit - ten, und las - se_ dich
- - low Thee al - so with joy - light-ened foot-steps, Nor stray from Thy

nicht,_____ mein Le - ben, mein Licht,_____ mein
sight,_____ My life and my light,_____ My

No. 14. Recitative

Evangelist

Der - sel - bi - ge Jün - ger war dem Ho - hen - prie - ster be - kannt, und
That oth - er dis - ci - ple to the high priest had long been known, and

[No. 14]

ging mit Je - su hin - ein in des Ho - hen - prie - sters Pa - last,
went with Je - sus with-in to the pal - ace of the high priest.

Pe - trus a - ber stund drau-ssen vor der Tür. Da ging der an - de - re
But with-out, at the door-way, Pe - ter stood. Then did the oth - er dis-

Jün - ger, der dem Ho - hen - prie - ster be - kannt war, hin - aus, und
ci - ple, who was known to them in the pal - ace, go out, and

re - de - te mit der Tür - hü - te - rin und füh - re - te Pe - trum hin - ein.
spake un - to her that tend - ed the door, and brought al - so Pe - ter with-in.

29

Tem-pel, da al-le Ju-den zu-sam-men kom-men, und ha-be nichts im Ver-borg'nen ge-
tem-ple where all the Jews al-ways come to-geth-er, and have said noth-ing in se-cret at

31

red't. Was fra-gest du mich dar-um?   Fra-ge die dar-um, die ge-hö-ret ha-ben, was ich zu
all. Why ask-est thou this of me?   Rath-er ask of them who have heard my teaching what sort of

34

ih-nen ge-re-det ha-be;   sie-he,   die-sel-bi-gen wis-sen, was
thing it was I taught them.   See now,   they sure-ly re-mem-ber the

36   **Evangelist**

ich ge-sa-get ha-be!   Als er a-ber sol-ches re-de-te, gab der Die-ner ei-ner, die
whole of what I taught them.   But when Je-sus thus had spo-ken,   a man servant standing

No. 15. Chorale

Wer hat dich so ge - schla - gen, mein Heil, und dich mit
Who was it dared to smite Thee, Thy good with ill re -

Pla - gen so ü - bel zu - ge - richt't? Du
quite Thee, So foul - ly treat - ed Thee? For

bist ja nicht ein Sün - der, wie wir und un - sre
Thou art no of - fen - der, Nor didst to sin sur -

Kin - der, von Mis - se - ta - ten weisst du nicht.
ren - der, From e - vil - do - ing Thou art free.

[No. 15]

13
Ich, ich und mei - ne Sün - den, die sich wie Körn - lein
Mine, mine the sins of - fend - ing, Which are like grains un -

16
fin - den des San - des an dem Meer, die
end - ing Of sand up - on the shore; These

19
ha - ben dir er - re - get das E - lend, das dich
sins it was that brought Thee Thy mis - er - y, and

22
schlä - get, und das be - trüb - te Mar - ter - heer.
wrought Thee Of mar - tyr - dom the aw - ful store.

No. 16. Recitative

No. 17. Chorus

* In BG there is no change of time-signature from the **C** of the preceding recitative. See p. x.

42262 In BG, also, only two sharps are in the signature, the G# being added as an accidental wherever needed.

No. 18. Recitative

*In BG only two sharps are in the signature, the G# being indicated as an accidental wherever needed.

Servant — Evangelist

Ohr ab-ge-hau-en hat-te: Sa-he ich dich nicht im Gar-ten bei ihm? Da ver-
smit-ten and cut his ear off: Did I not see thee in the gar-den with him? Then did

leug-ne-te Pe-trus a-ber-mal, und al - so-bald krä-he-te der Hahn.
Pe-ter de-ny it a third time, and straight-way the cock be-gan his crowing.

[or omit & play
l. h. alone]

Da ge-dach-te Pe-trus an die Wor-te Je-su, und ging hin-
Then did Pe-ter bring to mind the word of Je-sus, and he went

Adagio

aus und wei - - - - ne-te bit-ter-lich, und wei-
out be-wail - - - - ing it bit-ter - ly, be-wail-

No. 19. Aria

Tenor

[p. 70]

*The rhythm ♩. ♪ in this aria should always be played (and sung) approximately as ♪..♪ , in accordance with the prevailing practice in Bach's time, except where the simultaneous occurrence of four even 16ths *in the same hand* makes this impractical. Thus the left hand plays ♪..♪ everywhere. Measure 31, for example, should be played (and sung):

No. 20. Chorale

Pe-trus, der nicht denkt zu - rück, sei - nen Gott ver - nei - net,
Pe-ter, while his con-science slept, Thrice de-nied his Sav - iour,

der doch auf ein'n ern-sten Blick bit-ter-lich - en wei - net:
When it woke he bit-ter wept At his base be - ha - vior.

Je - su, bli - cke mich auch an, wenn ich nicht will bü - ssen;
Je - sus, let not me for - get; True de - vo - tion teach me;

wenn ich Bö - ses hab' ge-tan, rüh - re mein Ge - wis - sen.
When on e - vil I am set, Through my con-science reach me.

End of Part I

Part II
No. 21. Chorale

Chri- stus, der uns se- lig macht, kein Böss hat be - gan- gen,
Christ, through whom we all are blest, Knew no e- vil- do- ing.

der ward für uns in der Nacht als ein Dieb ge- fan- gen,
Him at night did they ar- rest, Like a thief pur- su- ing,

ge- führt vor gott- lo- se Leut' und fälsch- lich ver- kla- get,
Led be- fore the god- less throng And false- ly con- vict- ed,

ver- lacht, ver- höhnt und ver- speit, wie denn die Schrift sa - get.
Laughed at, scoffed at, spat up- on, As the Word pre- dict- ed.

No. 22. Recitative

No. 23. Chorus

*In BG, the flat is not in the signature, but is added wherever needed as an accidental.

[No. 23]

No. 24. Recitative

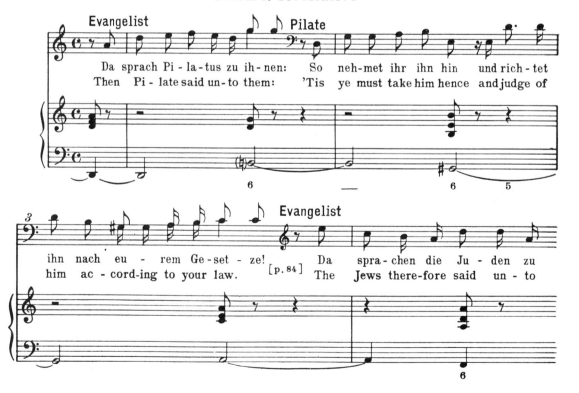

No. 25. Chorus

*No satisfactory reduction of all the orchestra material being practical, two different right-hand parts are given. In performance without orchestra, the upper line will be essential; in rehearsal, the lower of the two may be found preferable.

[No. 25]

[No. 25]

No. 26. Recitative

[No. 26]

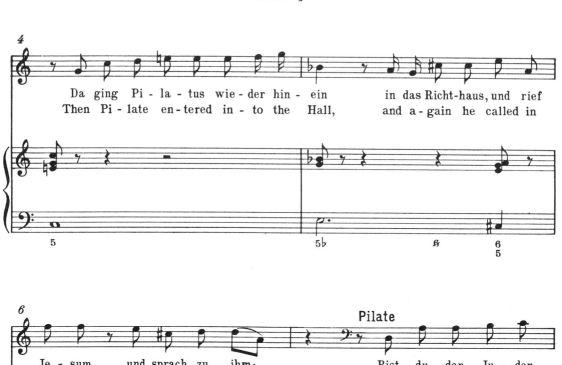

Da ging Pi-la-tus wie-der hin-ein in das Richt-haus, und rief
Then Pi-late en-tered in-to the Hall, and a-gain he called in

Je-sum, und sprach zu ihm: Bist du der Ju-den
Je-sus, and said to him: Art thou the King of

Pilate

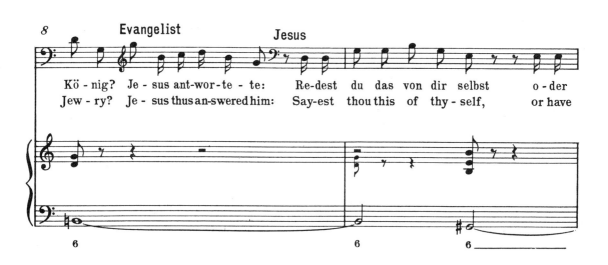

Evangelist

Jesus

Kö-nig? Je-sus ant-wor-te-te: Re-dest du das von dir selbst o-der
Jew-ry? Je-sus thus an-swered him: Say-est thou this of thy-self, or have

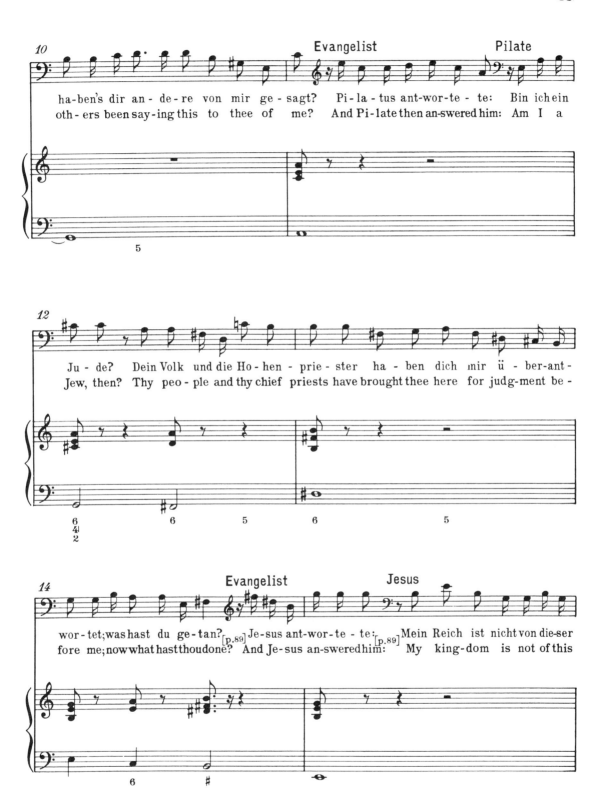

16

Welt, wä - re mein Reich von die - ser Welt, mei - ne Die-ner wür-den dar - ob __

world; for were my king-dom of this world, then my servants all would fight to de-

18

kämp - - fen, dass ich den Ju - den nicht ü - ber-ant-wor-tet

fend _____ me, that I should not un - to the Jews be de-

20

wür - de! a - ber, nun ist mein Reich nicht von dan - nen.

liv - ered. Nay then, but not from hence is my king-dom. [p. 89]

No. 27. Chorale

Ach gro - sser Kö - nig, gross zu al - len
O might - y King, al - might - y through all

Zei - ten, wie kann ich g'nug - sam die - se Treu' aus -
a - ges, How shall I fit - ly strive to sing Thy

brei - ten? Kein's Men - schen Her - ze mag in - des aus -
prais - es? No mor - tal heart can ev - er hope to

den - ken, was dir zu schen - - ken.
show Thee What it doth owe Thee.

* C♯? BG prints both stanzas under the same staves, with a repeat sign, and thus has C♯ both times.
C♯ directly followed by C♮ is of course perfectly possible (that succession occurs two measures earlier); but perhaps C♮ at the end of the first stanza binds the two stanzas more closely together.

Ich kann's mit mei - nen Sin - nen nicht er -
My fee - ble tongue no coun - ter - part can

rei - chen, wo - mit doch dein Er - bar - men zu ver -
fash - ion With which it might com - pare Thy great com -

glei - chen. Wie kann ich dir denn dei - ne Lie - bes -
pas - sion. How can I thanks for Thy good deeds, so

ta - ten im Werk er - stat - ten?
ten - der, In works e'er ren - der?

No. 28. Recitative

*It seems not impossible that this passage was intended to be sung:

ich bin ein Kö-nig. Ich bin da-zu ge-bo-ren

*See footnote on p.71.

No. 29. Chorus

No. 30. Recitative

No. 31. Arioso

Bass

Adagio [♪ = 60-72; see pp. ix ff.]

2 Vle. d'amore

Lute

pianissimo *

Be -
Be -

trach - te, mei - ne Seel', mit ängst - li - chem Ver -
think thee, O —— my soul, in ag - o - ny and

gnü - gen, mit bit - t'rer Lust und halb be - klemmt von Her - zen, dein
rap - ture, What though thy heart with bit - ter joy doth lan - guish, The

*See p. xxxvi. **Concerning the German text of this Arioso, see p. 241.

a) See p. xxvi.

No. 32. Aria
Tenor

Un - ter - lass auf Ihn, ohn' Un - ter - lass, drum sieh ohn' Un - ter - lass auf
raise thine eyes to Him, nor cease _____ to raise thine eyes, to raise thine eyes to

Ihn.
Him. [p. 151]

[♪ = 84 - 96; see pp. ix ff.]
2 Vle. d'amore

[p]
'Cello & Organ (no Cb.)

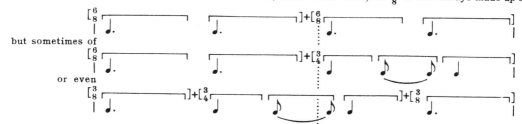

* To simplify the reading of these very long measures, a dotted bar-line has been added at the middle of each measure. Since, however, in the essential rhythms of this aria, the $\frac{12}{8}$ is not always made up of

but sometimes of

or even

brackets have been added to indicate the beats of the essential rhythms where they differ from the regular meter, or change within a measure.

Er - wä - ge,   er - wä - ge,   er - wä - - ge,   er -
Be - hold then,   be - hold then,   be - hold _____ then, be -

* ♩ 𝄾 ♩ 𝄾 in BG, in this measure only.

a)   b)

** The interruption of the 16th-beams is in BG, and if this is taken
from the MSS, some of which are autograph in this number, it shows
a method of Bach's for indicating phrasing: he used slurs mostly for
bowing and tonguing indications.

[No. 32]

[No. 32]

geht.
bove. [p. 201]

[*p*]

[No. 32]

30

steht. _____
Love. _____

[pp cresc.]   [p] [cresc.]

31

[3/4]   a)

mp

32 [3/4]

Da - ran,   nach - dem die Was - ser - wo
And see,   the waves of sin sub - sid

[pp]

33 [3/4]

- gen von ___ un - srer Sünd - flut sich ___ ver - zo -
- ing, Sun - beams a - gain dark clouds ___ di - vid -

a)
3

a) The precise meaning of the reverse curve on the end of the trill-sign as given in BG and reproduced here – if it had any precise meaning – is not clear. The context would perhaps call for what Couperin called a "pincé continu", something like: A similar ornament might be added in m. 13.

b)

No. 33. Recitative

Evangelist

Und die Kriegs-knech-te floch-ten ei - ne Kro - ne von Dor-nen, und
The sol-diers plait-ed then for him a crown out of thorns, and

setz-ten sie auf sein Haupt, und leg-ten ihmein Pur-pur-kleid an, und spra-chen:
put it up-on his head and put on him a robe of pur-ple, all say-ing:[p.111]

No. 34. Chorus

[♩=108-120; see pp.ix ff.]

Soprano

Sei ge - grü - sset, lie-ber Ju - den -
Lo, we hail thee, dear-est King of

Alto

Sei ge - grü - sset,
Lo, we hail thee,

Tenor

Sei ge -
Lo, we

Bass

[♩=108-120; see pp.ix ff.]

Fl.I* Ob.I

Fl.II Ob.II

Strgs.*

[No. 34]

[No. 34]

No. 35. Recitative

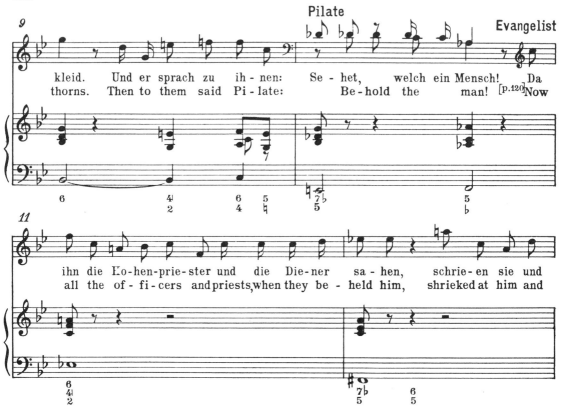

No. 36. Chorus

*It would do no great violence to Bach's music if when this work is sung in English the more natural rhythm {♪ ♪ ♪ / cru-ci-fy} were used here.

[No. 36]

* See footnote on p. 117.

No. 37. Recitative

Pi-la-tus sprach zu ih-nen: Neh-met ihr ihn hin und kreu-zi-get ihn; denn
And Pi-late thus made an-swer: Ye must take him hence and cru-ci - fy him, for

ich fin-de kei - ne Schuld an ihm! [p.129] Die Ju - den ant-wor-te - ten ihm: [p.129]
I find no fault in him at all. [p.129] The Jews straight-way an-swered and said: [p.129]

No. 38. Chorus

[♩=66-84; see pp. ix ff.]

Soprano

Alto

Tenor

Bass

Wir ha - ben ein Ge - setz, und nach dem Ge -
We have a sa - cred law, and who breaks that

[♩=66-84; see pp. ix ff.]

[mf]

[No. 38]

*The distribution of the German words in this chorus, as given in BG, is awkward and ineffective in several passages, and it has been changed in the present edition. BG doubtless reproduces faithfully what is in the MSS, but the latter are not autograph in this number and may not correctly represent Bach's considered purpose.

[No. 38]

ben, soll er ster - - - - - - - - -
ish, he must per - - - - - - - - -

ha - ben ein Ge - setz, und nach dem Ge - setz soll er
have a sa - cred law, and who breaks that law, he must

ster - - - - - - - - - -
per - - - - - - - - - -

ben, soll er ster - - - - - - - -
ish, he must per - - - - - - - -

ster - - - - - - - - -
per - - - - - - - - -

ben, denn er hat sich selbst zu Got - tes Sohn, zu Got - tes Sohn ge -
ish, for he made him - self to be the Son of God, the Son of

*BG has e' instead of f'; see p.241

No. 39. Recitative

[No. 39]

No. 40. Chorale

Durch dein Ge-fäng-nis, Got-tes Sohn, ist uns die Frei-heit kom-men,
Our free-dom, Son of God, a-rose When Thou wast cast in pris-on;

Dein Ker-ker ist der Gna-den-thron, die Frei-statt al-ler From-men,
And from the dur-ance Thou didst choose Our lib-er-ty is ris-en,

denn gingst du nicht die Knecht-schaft ein, müsst' un-s're Knecht-schaft e-wig sein.
Didst Thou not choose a slave to be, We all were slaves e-ter-nal-ly.

No. 41. Recitative

No. 42. Chorus

[No. 42]

[No. 42]

*Perhaps this should read [music notation] or [music notation]

*BG has G♮, doubtless by error.

*BG has d#′ instead of e′, as in the parallel measure of No.38.

42262

*BG has a quarter-note. a)

42262 (or omit)

No. 43. Recitative

Da Pi - la - tus das Wort hö - re - te, füh - re - te er Je - sum heraus, und
Now when Pi - late heard them speaking thus, straightway he brought Je - sus forth, and

setz - te sich auf den Richt - stuhl, an der Stät - te, die da hei - sset: Hoch -
took up his place up - on the seat of judg - ment, in a place called High

pfla - ster, auf E - brä - isch a - ber: Gab - ba - tha.__ Es war
Pave - ment, but in He - brew called Gab - ba - tha.__ And it

a - ber der Rüst - tag in O - stern, um die sech - ste Stun - de, und er spricht zu den
was a - bout the sixth hour of prep - a - ra - tion of the Pass - o - ver, and he saith to the

No.44. Chorus

[No. 44]

[No. 44]

*See footnote on p. 117.

No. 45. Recitative

No. 46. Chorus

*Perhaps Bach intended
the alto's first note to be A.

No. 47. Recitative

Evangelist

Da ü-ber-ant-wor-te-te er ihn, dass er ge-kreu-
Then Pi-late de-liv-ered him to them, that they might cru-

- -zi-get würde. Sie nah-men a-ber Je-sum und füh-re-ten ihn hin, und er
- -ci-fy him. Then took they Je-sus with them and led him a-way, and he

No. 48. Aria

Bass Solo and Chorus

[No. 48]

Bass Solo

Eilt, _____ eilt,
Run, _____ run,

eilt, eilt, ihr ___ an - ge - focht' - nen See - len, ihr ___
run, run, ye ___ souls whom ___ care op - press - es, ye ___

___ an - ge - focht' - nen See - len, eilt, ihr an - ge - focht' - -
___ souls whom ___ care op - press - es, run, ye souls whom care _____

[No. 48]

[No. 48]

[No. 48]

*See p. xxxv

No. 49. Recitative

Evangelist

All - da kreu - zig-ten sie ihn, und mit ihm zween an - de - re
And there cru - ci-fied they him, and two oth - ers with him

zu bei-den Sei-ten, Je-sum a-ber mit-ten in - ne. Pi - la-tus a - ber schrieb ei-ne
on ei-ther side, Je-sus in the midst, be-tween them. And Pi-late wrote for him an

Ü - ber-schrift, und setz - te sie auf das Kreuz, und war ge-schrie-ben:
ep - i-graph; and put it up-on the cross; and it was writ-ten:

Adagio [in tempo]   [Recit.]

Je - sus von Na - za-reth, der Ju-den Kö - nig! Die-se Ü-ber-schrift
Je - sus of Naz - a-reth, the King of Jew - ry!* And this ep-i-graph was

*In concert performance, "Judah" may be more readily understood, although of course Judah was
42262 only one part of the land of the Jews.

11

la - sen viel Ju - den, denn die Stät - te war na - he bei der Stadt, da Je - sus ge -
read by man - y, for the town was not far from the place where Je - sus was

13

kreu - - zi - get ist. Und es war ge - schrie - ben auf e -
cru - - ci - fied. And the words were writ - ten in the

15

brä - i - sche, grie - chi - sche und la - tei - ni - sche Spra - che.
He - brew, the Lat - in, and the Gre - cian tongues.

17

Da spra - chen die Ho - hen - prie - ster der Ju - den zu Pi - la - to:
Then said the chief priests of the Jews un - to Pi - late.[p.168]

No. 50. Chorus

* Compare the 3/2 groupings suggested in No. 34, most of which are equally applicable here.

42262 ** See footnote on p. 79. *** See footnote on p. 163.

[No. 50]

*Original German word distribution: der Juden König, ich bin der Juden König.

42262

No. 51. Recitative

Evangelist: Pi - la - tus ant - wor - tet: Pilate: Was ich ge - schrie - ben
But Pi - late re - plied to them: [p.169] Be - hold, what I have

ha - be, das ha - be ich ge - schrie - ben.
writ - ten, that is what I have writ - ten.

No. 52. Chorale

In mei - nes Her - zens Grun - de, dein Nam' und Kreuz al - lein Fun -
In my heart's in - most ker - nel Thy Name and Cross a - lone Glow

kelt all' Zeit und Stun - de, drauf kann ich fröh - lich sein. Er -
bright with light e - ter - nal, And bring me joys un - known. O —

schein' mir in dem Bil - de zu Trost in mei - ner Not, wie
come, bright vi - sion, ren - der Me com - fort in my need, Since

du, — Herr Christ, so mil - de, dich hast ge - blut't zu Tod.
Je - sus, mild and ten - der, For us to death did bleed.

No. 53. Recitative

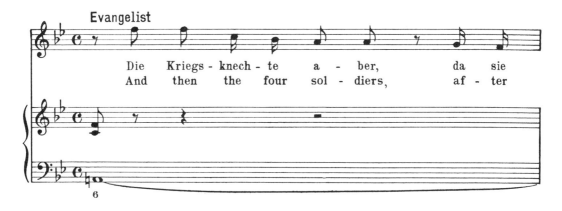

Evangelist

Die Kriegs - knech - te a - ber, da sie
And then the four sol - diers, af - ter

[No. 53]

No. 54. Chorus

*Optional accompaniment

In the original, flutes, oboes, violins, and violas double the voice parts, while the 'cello has the continuous 16th-notes, and the bass and organ the quarter-notes here represented by down-stems in the left hand.

42262

[No. 54]

[No. 54]

[No. 54]

No. 55. Recitative

No. 56. Chorale

Er nahm al - les wohl in Acht in der letz - ten Stun - de,
He of ev - 'ry - thing took heed In his hour of dy - ing,

sei - ne Mut - ter noch be - dacht', setzt ihr ein'n Vor - mun - de.
Car - ing for his moth - er's need, On his friend re - ly - ing.

O Mensch, ma - che Rich - tig - keit, Gott und Men - schen lie - be,
O Man, lead a right - eous life, Love God and thy neigh - bor,

stirb dar - auf ohn' al - les Leid, und dich nicht be - trü - be.
Death will bring an end to strife, Rest from care and la - bor.

No. 57. Recitative

Evangelist

Und von Stund' an nahm sie der Jün-ger zu sich.
And from then on she stayed with that dis-ci-ple.

Dar-nach, als Je-sus wuss-te, dass schon al - les voll-bracht war, dass die
And now since Je-sus knew full well that all was ac-com-plished, as was

Schrift er-fül-let wür-de, spricht er: **Jesus** Mich dür-stet! **Evangelist** Da
writ-ten in the Scrip-ture, he saith: I thirst!__ Now some

stund ein Ge-fä-sse voll Es-sigs. Sie fül-le-ten a-ber ei-nen Schwamm mit
vin-e-gar stood in a ves-sel. They filled a sponge with vin-e-gar from the

Es-sig und leg-ten ihn um ei-nen I-sop-pen und hiel-ten es ihm dar zum
ves-sel, and put it on a twig of hys-sop, and put it to his mouth to

Mun-de. Da nun Je-sus den Es-sig ge-nom-men
drink it. When the vin-e-gar had touched the lips of

Jesus

hat-te, sprach er: [p.190] Es ist voll-bracht!
Je-sus, he said: It is ful-filled.

42262

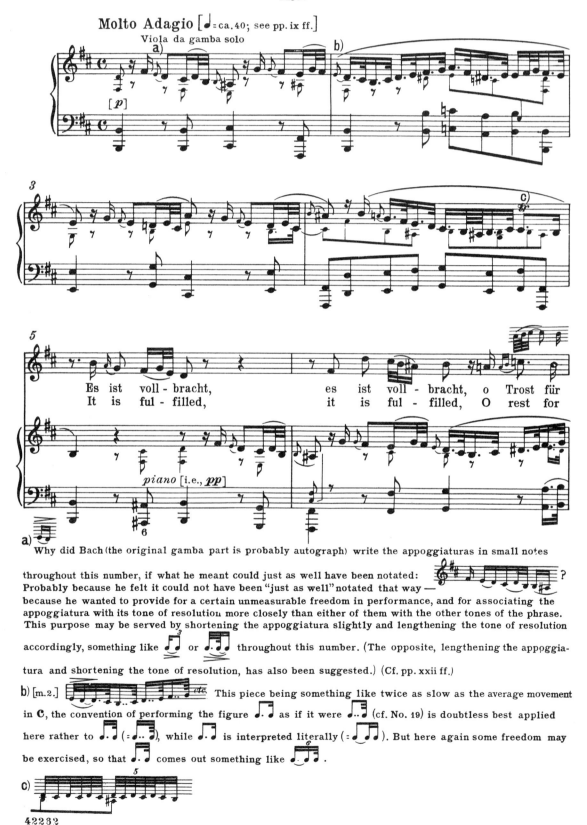

No. 58. Aria

Alto

Molto Adagio [♩ = ca. 40; see pp. ix ff.]

Viola da gamba solo

[p]

Es ist voll - bracht,   es ist voll - bracht, o Trost für
It is ful - filled,   it is ful - filled, O rest for

piano [i.e., pp]

a) Why did Bach (the original gamba part is probably autograph) write the appoggiaturas in small notes throughout this number, if what he meant could just as well have been notated: ? Probably because he felt it could not have been "just as well" notated that way — because he wanted to provide for a certain unmeasurable freedom in performance, and for associating the appoggiatura with its tone of resolution more closely than either of them with the other tones of the phrase. This purpose may be served by shortening the appoggiatura slightly and lengthening the tone of resolution accordingly, something like   or   throughout this number. (The opposite, lengthening the appoggiatura and shortening the tone of resolution, has also been suggested.) (Cf. pp. xxii ff.)

b) [m. 2.]   This piece being something like twice as slow as the average movement in **C**, the convention of performing the figure   as if it were   (cf. No. 19) is doubtless best applied here rather to   (=   ), while   is interpreted literally (=   ). But here again some freedom may be exercised, so that   comes out something like   .

c)

a) BG has no appoggiatura here,
perhaps through an oversight.

42262

und schliesst den Kampf, _____ und schliesst den Kampf, _____
and ends the strife, _____ and ends the strife, _____

piano

_____ und schliesst den Kampf, _____
and ends the strife, _____

der Held aus Ju - da siegt mit Macht, der
Vic - to - rious Ju - dah's he - ro fights, Vic -

forte

piano

Held aus Ju - da siegt mit Macht, _____
to - rious Ju - dah's he - ro fights _____

*BG has E instead of F#

42262

38

Adagio [i.e., tempo primo]

— und schliesst den Kampf, und schliesst den Kampf. Es ist voll-bracht.
— and ends the strife, and ends the strife. It is ful-filled.

forte

[p]

41

43

a) Es ist voll-bracht.
It is ful-filled.

a) b)

No. 59. Recitative

Evangelist

Und neig - te das Haupt und ver - schied.
And bowed down his head, and was gone. [p.200]

6 5

6 5
4 #

No. 60. Aria
Bass Solo and Chorus

[No. 60]

[No. 60]

*BG notates the appoggiatura by the little slur alone("accento"); see p. xxiii.

[No. 60]

39

du das Haupt _____ und sprichst still - schwei-gend: Ja, still - schwei-gend, still -
Thou Thy head _____ to say, in si - lence: Yea! in si - lence, in _

41

schwei-gend: Ja! doch nei - gest du das Haupt und sprichst still - schwei - gend:
si - lence: Yea! Yet bow-est Thou Thy head to say, in _ si - lence:

43

Ja!
Yea!

No. 61. Recitative

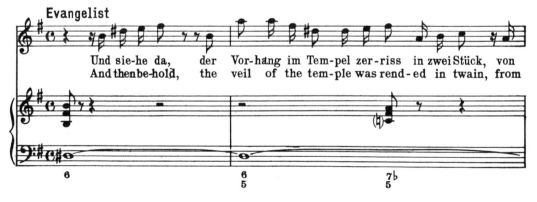

Evangelist

Und sie-he da, der Vor-hang im Tem-pel zer-riss in zwei Stück, von
And then be-hold, the veil of the tem-ple was rend-ed in twain, from

No. 62. Arioso

Tenor

[No.62]

No. 63. Aria

Soprano

Zer - flie - sse, mein Her - ze, in
Re - lease, O— my spir - it, thy

*Only three flats are in the BG signature, the D♭ being added as an accidental wherever needed.

a)

Höch - - - sten zu Eh - ren,
High - - - est is dy - ing.

zer - flie - sse, mein Her - ze, in Flu - ten der Zäh -
Re - lease, O my spir - it, thy tor - rents of cry -

- ren, dem Höch-sten zu Eh - - - -
- ing: The High-est is dy - - - -

ren.
ing.

forte
[i.e. mp]

[No. 63]

tot!
dead!

dein   Je - sus ist _ tot,   tot,   tot! ____ dein
Thy   Je - sus is _ dead,   dead,   dead! ___ Thy

Je - sus   ist   tot, __   tot, __   dein ____ Je - sus ist
Je - sus   is   dead,   dead,   Thy ____ Je - sus is

tot.
dead!

* The ♭ before D is apparently omitted in the MSS, doubtless by oversight.
** In BG, the voice, flutes, and oboi da caccia have only an undotted 8th-note
here.

[No. 63]

No. 64. Recitative

Evangelist

Die Ju - den a - ber, die - weil es der Rüst-tag war, dass
The Chief Priests there-fore, be - cause of the Pass-o - ver, in

nicht die Leich-na - me am Kreu-ze blie - ben den Sab-bat ü - ber (denn des-
or - der that the bod-ies should not re - main on the cross for the Sab-bath (for the

sel - bi-gen Sa - bat-tags war sehr gross), ba - ten sie Pi - la - tum, dass
Sab-bath in that week was a high one), now en - treat - ed Pi - late to al-

*The markings *piano* and *forte*, from the original MSS, undoubtedly point simply to a differentiation between the parenthetical "aside" and the direct narration.

ih - re Bei - ne ge-bro-chen, und sie ab - ge - nom-men wür - den;
low their legs to be bro-ken, that they might from thence be ta - ken.

da ka-men die Kriegs-kne-chte und bra-chen dem er-sten die Bei - ne, und dem
Then came the sol - diers and brake the legs of the first one, and the

an-dern, der mit ihm ge-kreu - zi - get war. Als sie a - ber zu Je - su
oth - er which was cru-ci-fied there with him. Then at last com-ing up to

ka - men, da sie sa - hen, dass er schon ge-stor-ben war, bra - chen sie
Je - sus, and per-ceiv-ing that he had al - read-y died, there-fore they

15

ihm die Bei - ne nicht; son-dern der Kriegs-knechte ei - ner er-öff-ne-te sei - ne
brake not Je - sus' legs: but one of the sol - diers then took up his spear, and with the

17

Sei - te mit ei - nem Speer, und al - so - bald ging Blut und Was - ser her-
spear did he pierce His side, and straightway came there blood and wa - ter

19

aus. Und der das ge - se - hen hat, der hat es be-zeu-get, und sein Zeug-nis ist
out. And he that hath seen these things, 'tis he who bare rec-ord, and his rec - ord is

21

wahr, und der-sel - bi-ge weiss, dass er die Wahr-heit sa - get, auf dass ihr
true, nor in-deed can he fail to know where - of he speak-eth, that ye be-

No. 65. Chorale

O hilf, Chri-ste, Got-tes Sohn, durch dein bit-tres Lei-den,
Help, O Je-sus, God's own Son, Through thy bit-ter an-guish,

dass wir, dir stets un-ter-tan, all' Un-tu-gend mei-den:
That the fa-vor Thou hast won E-vil deeds may van-quish.

dei-nen Tod und sein' Ur-sach' frucht-bar-lich be-den-ken,
How and why our Sav-iour died We must pon-der tru-ly,

da-für, wie-wohl arm und schwach, dir Dank-o-pfer schen-ken. schen-ken.
And, though weak, leave naught un-tried, Lord, to thank Thee du-ly. du-ly.

*In BG, only three flats are in the signature, the D♭ and G♭ being added as accidentals wherever needed.

No. 66. Recitative

gra - ben.   Es war a - ber an der Stät - te,   da er ge-
bur - y.   In Gol - go-tha,where the place was   where He was

kreu - zi - get ward, ein Gar - ten,   und im Gar - ten ein neu Grab, in wel - ches
cru - ci - fied, was a gar - den,   and in the gar - den a   new grave   in which

nie - mand je ge - le - gen war,   da - selbst hin leg - ten sie Je - sum,   um des
no man yet had e'er been laid.   And   there-in   then laid they Je - sus,   since it

Rüst - tags wil - len der Ju - den, die - weil das Grab na - he war.
was the day of prep-ar - a - tion, it be - ing so nigh __ at hand.

No. 67. Chorus

*In BG, only two flats are in the signature, the A♭ being added as an accidental wherever needed.

42262

No. 68. Chorale

Ach Herr, lass dein lieb' En - ge - lein am letz - ten End' die
O Lord, Thy lit - tle_ an - gel send, When - e'er my mor - tal

See - le mein in A - bra - hams Schoss tra - gen! Den
life shall end, To bear my soul to Heav - en! My

Leib in sein'm Schlaf - käm - mer - lein gar sanft, ohn' ein' - ge
bod - y in its_ cham - ber sleep, All tor - ment do_ Thou

Qual und Pein, ruhn bis am jüng - sten Ta - ge! Als -
dis - tant keep, Till Thy last call_ be giv - en! And

15
dann vom Tod' er - we - cke mich, dass mei - ne Au - gen se - hen dich in
then from death a - wak - en me, That these poor eyes their Lord may see, See,

19
al - ler Freud, o Got - tes Sohn, mein Hei - land und Ge -
Son of God, Thy glo - rious face, My ·Sav - iour and my

22
na - den - thron! Herr Je - su Christ, er - hö - re mich, er -
fount of grace! Lord Je - sus Christ, O hear Thou me, O

25
hö - re mich, ich will dich prei - sen e - wig - lich.
hear Thou me, Thee will I praise e - ter - nal - ly.

FOREWORD TO THE BACH-GESELLSCHAFT EDITION OF THE ST. JOHN PASSION (Jahrg. XII')

By Wilhelm Rust

[Material concerning other BG volumes has been omitted; also material concerning details of the German text and its origin, since presumably these would be of interest mainly to those who can read the BG Foreword in the original. All omissions are indicated.—A. M.]

SOURCES:

A) The Original Score
B) A copy of the score from the collection of Count Voss
C) The Original Parts

All sources now [1863] property of the Royal Library in Berlin [later the Preussische Staats-Bibliothek; now the Öffentliche wissenschaftliche Bibliothek].

A) THE ORIGINAL SCORE. Autograph caption on the first page of music:

"J. J. Passio secundum Joannem

à 4 Voci, 2 Oboe, 2 Violini, Viola è Cont. di J. S. Bach."

[The editor here points out that in previous volumes of BG, the term "original" had been used for scores in Bach's handwriting, but now a distinction must be made between "original" and "autograph".]

The only portions of the original score of the St. John Passion that are in Bach's handwriting are the first twenty pages [No. 1 to No. 14, m. 42½]. [But Spitta later stated that only the first ten pages of the original score were in Bach's handwriting: these are the pages that are reproduced in facsimile in Jahrg. XLIV of BG, and include only No. 1 and the first 11 measures of No. 2.] There are, however, authentic indications throughout the score that answer with a definite affirmative the question of whether the autograph pages and the copyist's work belong together and make up an original, single score. We find the characteristic traits of Bach's handwriting first of all in a continuous and complete pagination, beginning with page 1 and ending with page 92. This could appropriately be termed an external revision, and the cipher *"Fine | D[omino]. J[esu]. C[hristo]. C[um]. Gl[oria]."* the affixed attesting seal. In addition, we find Bach's correcting and supplementing hand as follows:

No. 19, viola part: see list of Divergences in Detail.

No. 30, m. 3: fourth quarter, supplying two missing groups of triplets in the voice part.

No. 58, mm. 21-39; No. 60, mm. 21-28; No. 63, m. 59, etc.: various expression marks, such as *forte, piano,* and trill signs.

No. 60, m. 21 with three preceding 8ths; mm. 26-29; No. 67, mm. 73-78: various additions to the continuo.

Finally, his hand shows itself in a vigorous *"Volti"* ["turn" (the page)] at the end of p. 81 of the original score, which falls at No. 63, m. 118.

B) THE COPY OF THE SCORE FROM THE COLLECTION OF COUNT VOSS

This copy shows itself throughout to be a true copy of the original score. A choir-singer of C. P. E. Bach's, named Hering, whose copies of Bach's works have won for themselves a well-founded reputation, made this copy also. It contains some ununderstandable individual corrections in an unknown hand, which were mostly completed by the scraping-knife, and turn out always to be changes for the worse from the original reading. Of special value for the BG edition was the reliable figuring [of the continuo; but see pp. xxxi-xxxiv].

C) THE ORIGINAL PARTS

They fall into three groups, according to date: (1) early; (2) middle; (3) late. Together they make a considerable number. Nevertheless, on closer examination one finds that there are certain gaps. Apart from a few unimportant parts (e.g., that of Pilate), as well as the obbligato violoncello for the chorus No. 54, the loss of the "early" figured organ part is especially regrettable. The surviving figured part belongs to the late set; it has many gaps and is in general not at all reliable. We were therefore compelled to go back to the copy of the score already described under B) above. Its general reliability warrants the assumption that the copyist had before him when he wrote it (before 1788, the year of C. P. E. Bach's death*) the original figuring. In the course of its various journeys back and forth between Hamburg and Berlin, etc., the part must have been lost subsequent to that time.

The following is a list of the surviving parts, their autograph portions being indicated in italics. J. S. Bach's revisions and corrections are to be found throughout these parts:

(1) Earlier parts, listing those portions deemed in Bach's handwriting:

Traversière [Flute] I: *No. 1; also Nos. 50-62.*

Traversière II: *Nos. 1-15; also No. 50 to about the middle of No. 67.*

Hautbois I & II: *Nos. 1-7; also No. 62.*

Violino Ia: *No. 1, from about m. 72 to the end; No. 19, mm. 1-14; also an insert for Nos. 31-32, which, like a later autograph passage for No. 50, has to do with a change in instrumentation.*

Violino IIa:** *No. 1, last four measures; No. 62; also an insert serving the same purpose as the insert in Violino I.*

Viola a: *Nos. 1-9; also 12 measures in the final chorus.*

Viola da gamba, which occurs only in No. 58, *is autograph throughout.*

Soprano Concertante: *No. 1 (complete).****

Alto Concertante: *No. 1 (complete).****

Tenore, Evangelista: *No. 1 (complete);**** *No. 66, mm. 6-8.*

Tenore, Servus: *autograph throughout.*

Basso, Jesus: *No. 1 (complete);**** *No. 31.* [N.B. If the bulk of this part belongs among the "early" parts, then No. 31 must be an insert, as in Violins I & II.—A. M.]

Continuo a: *No. 1, mm. 51-No. 3, m. 2; also Nos. 31-37.* [N. B. If the bulk of this part belongs among the "early" parts, then Nos. 31 & 32 must have been added later.—A. M.]

---

*An "autograph" score and a set of parts were listed in the inventory of C. P. E. Bach's estate published in Hamburg in 1790.—A. M.

**BG says Ib at this point, but must mean IIa, since Ib is listed under (2), the "middle" set of parts.—A. M.

***No. 1 was pasted into these parts at the time the middle group of parts was made, according to Spitta.—A. M.

(2) Middle parts:

Soprano, Alto, Tenore, Basso in Ripieno [i.e., *choral parts only*].

Violino I*b*, Violino II*b*, Continuo *b* (pro Bassono grosso), Organo ò cembalo (obbligato). *The last-named part, belonging to No. 31* [only] *is autograph throughout. In Violino Ib, the Chorale No. 20 is autograph.*

(3) Later parts:

Violino I*c*, Viola *b*, Continuo *c* (pro cembalo) figured, Continuo *d* (pro cembalo) unfigured. [N. B. The two Continuo parts *c* and *d* are in the same key as the other parts, while Continuo *a* is transposed a tone downward, according to Terry, *Bach's Orchestra*, p. 234. Such transposed parts were always made for the organ, which was at the old, high, choir pitch. The BG editor apparently jumped to the conclusion that the untransposed parts were for harpsichord; but Schering in his *Johann Sebastian Bachs Leipziger Kirchenmusik* has shown that this does not follow. There is no clear indication that Bach ever used the harpsichord to accompany anything in the St. John Passion except No. 31, where on one occasion it may have substituted for the lute.—A. M.]

The interrelations of all this material, the occasional added indications, the omission and interpolation of whole movements—all this gives us an instructive and interesting glimpse into the master's workshop, and shows us how unceasing Bach was in his efforts to bring his work to the greatest possible perfection. Before the final version these efforts can be grouped in three periods, a different version of the work belonging to each period. Two of these versions are reflected in the parts; the third is contained in the original score. Considerable changes occur in addition to these three principal versions, it is true; but they seem to have been brought about more by passing circumstances than by the desire to improve the work.

Let us glance first at the three principal versions, and then at these incidental changes of secondary significance. Some remarks about changes that do not stem from Bach may follow.

The three principal versions differ mainly in the lyric [i.e., non-biblical] portions of the work. Apart from various emendations in the voice-leading, the [dramatic] core of the work remained untouched. The second version, then, differs from the first in that a whole group of lyric movements were deleted from the work and replaced by others. The external form of the whole was now completed in its final shape. The third version exhibits mainly internal improvements, the final polishing of certain details. This is visible principally in the autograph portions of the original score, while the remaining portions of that score, in a copyist's hand, are useful mainly for showing Bach's final intentions concerning instrumentation.

The movements occurring in the original version and removed by Bach are as follows:

(1) The introductory chorus *O Mensch, bewein' dein' Sünde gross* (E♭, $\frac{4}{4}$). Transposed to E major, this movement was incorporated in the second version of the St. Matthew Passion, where it crowns the first part of that work as its final chorus.

(2) An aria *Himmel reisse, Welt erbebe*, with a chorale cantus firmus [*Jesu, deine Passion*], which followed the Chorale No. 15 (this aria published in the appendix [to BG XII[1]]).

(3) A [tenor] aria *Zerschmettert mich, ihr Felsen und ihr Hügel*, later replaced by the aria *Ach mein Sinn*, No. 19 (the earlier aria published in the appendix [to BG XII[1]]).

(4) A [tenor] aria *Windet euch nicht so, geplagte Seelen*, later replaced by the bass arioso, *Betrachte, meine Seel'* and the tenor aria *Erwäge*, Nos. 31 and 32 (the earlier aria published in the appendix [to BG XII¹]).

(5) A figured chorale *Christe, du Lamm Gottes*. This chorale, which has been [erroneously] listed in various places as an independent chorus, now forms the conclusion of the cantata *Du wahrer Gott und Davids Sohn*, No. 23. (See p. xx of the foreword to BG V¹).

The new movements distinguishing the second version may be listed almost automatically, from the listing of the replaced older movements. Nevertheless, for the sake of completeness, we give them here:

(1) The introductory chorus *Herr, unser Herrscher;* (2) the tenor aria *Ach mein Sinn;* (3) the arioso *Betrachte, meine Seel';* (4) the tenor aria *Erwäge;* (5) the final chorale *Ach, Herr, lass dein' lieb' Engelein.*

From the fact that the original introductory chorus of the St. John was transferred to the St. Matthew, it ought to be possible to delimit fairly exactly the date of the second version, at least from one direction. But we cannot make the definite assumption that the sole reason for writing the new portions was the decision to use the old portions in other works. What does seem more than probable is that Bach would already have used the chorus *O Mensch, bewein' dein' Sünde gross* in the "first" version of the St. Matthew, in 1729, if he had already composed the new introductory chorus for the St. John, and had thus had the older chorus free for such use. Thus we date the composition of the five "new" movements listed above as probably later than 1729.*

To make clear to the reader the nature of the improvements contained in the third version, we must look a little more closely at some details of the second version. A comparison of the latter with the present [BG] score (which of course follows the third and last version), makes the later and better readings easy to distinguish:

No. 1, opening: In the second version, all the instruments that play the continuo line had steady 8th-notes. The indication that only the celli and bassoon [BG: "bassoons"] should have this rhythm, and that organ and contrabass [BG: "contrabasses"] should have the slower rhythm, is an improvement belonging to the third version, very clearly indicated in the original score [autograph at this point; reproduced in facsimile in BG XLIV].

No. 1, m. 58: The frequent markings of *piano, forte,* and *legato* from this point on are entirely lacking in the second version.

Nos. 3 and 5: In the second version, the oboes were in unison with Violin II and Viola (except for a few minor divergences).

No. 13, m. 157 etc.: In the second version, the whole introduction was repeated at the end of the aria.

These examples, striking enough, may suffice. Less striking are a great number of differences in voice-leading, particularly in the inner voices of the opening chorus. As samples, we submit the following passages from the earlier recitatives, and, to conclude the comparisons, the chorale [No. 9] *Dein Will' gescheh', Herr Gott*, in the forms in which they appear in Bach's first and second versions:

---

*Spitta's later researches brought him to different conclusions.–A.M.

No. 2, m. 6   No. 2, m. 8   No. 4, m. 8   No. 10, m. 6

wusste den Ort auch etc.   Da nun Ju-das etc.   Da frag-te er sie a-ber-mal: Schwä-her, wel-cher des Jahres Ho-her-

No. 10, m. 9

prie-ster war etc.   es wü-re gut, dass ein Mensch wür-de umbracht für das Volk.

Chorale [No. 9]

These are the three essential changes in the work.

Of the changes of a secondary nature it has already been stated that they seem to have been occasioned less by an intention to improve the work than by passing circumstances. These include all divergences of instrumentation that occur in the parts, belonging accordingly to the middle period. These changes were made, discarded, retained in one place but not in another, according to changing conditions. For the present day [1863], in which we are often not a little embarrassed by the requirements of Bach's instrumentation, the listing of these divergences will be of double value. For they are the master's own signals of how to proceed in similar cases. We find then:

In Nos. 31-32: two violins with mutes, instead of the viole d'amore.

In No. 32: the indication *"senza violone"*.

In Nos. 34 and 50: a reinforcement of the two oboes by some ("not all") of the violins.

In No. 58, mm. 20-40: a doubling of the voice part in the lower octave by the viola da gamba.

In No. 60: a reinforcement of the choral parts by some violins and violas.

In No. 62: two oboi d'amore instead of the oboi da caccia.

In No. 63: a muted violin (probably solo) instead of the flute [flutes?].

236

Finally, a reinforcement of the continuo parts by a "Continuo pro Bassono grosso". The latter plays in all the choruses and chorales, as well as in the first sixteen and last three measures of No. 19, in the forte passages of No. 48, and in the middle section of No. 58 [referred to by the BG editor as the "Vivace" section, although the BG score bears only the indication "Alla breve" at this point (cf. p. 188)].

A change of a different sort, which also belongs to a relatively early period, "between" the middle and the later parts, was the interpolation of a "Sinfonia" in place of the recitative, arioso, and aria, Nos. 61-63. Of this Sinfonia not a note survives. But its appearance and disappearance still attracts our attention to this extent: it combines with the rest of the material to prove with certainty that four performances of the St. John Passion took place in Bach's time; the first in the original version, the next in the second version, at the time from which the middle parts date; the third after this time, with the interpolated Sinfonia; the fourth without the Sinfonia again, at the time of the late parts. It is only after these late parts that no further external alterations took place. Whether a performance of the third version, represented by the "original" score, ever took place remains questionable.

Among all these changes, of major or minor importance, there are also some of which the authenticity as original must be seriously questioned, and some which are obviously not authentic. Among the latter is an interpolation containing the tenor aria *Erwäge* (No. 32) with many ornaments and with alterations in the text. In this nothing seems to be authentic. At any rate, a mutilated [*zerschnittenes*] sheet, bearing this apparently false material on one side, and on the other the end of the same aria in Bach's handwriting, must awaken suspicion. [The BG Foreword goes on to discuss changes in the text, and the authorship and circumstances of composition of the aria texts.]

Editorial Procedures [in BG]

After the [BG] editor had achieved a clear and definite picture of the original material, described at length above, no doubt remained concerning the nature of the editorial work to be done. Whereas usually in Bach's works when score and parts disagree it is the parts that exhibit the later and improved readings, the situation here is just the reverse. For establishing the basic reading of the work, the "original" score necessarily remained the one and only source. The parts could be drawn on only for the following supplementary purposes:

(1) The addition of the thorough bass figuring.

(2) The determination of the instrumentation, when the score here and there lacked precise indications. (The instances in which the instrumentation in the parts conflicts with that indicated in the "original" score have been mentioned above.)

(3) The correction of many errors occurring in the copyist's portions of the "original" score. Bach's proof-reading and revision of the score seems not to have gone very deep, but rather to have consisted of no more than a first glancing through.

(4) The addition of many missing performance indications and ornaments. Performance indications are sparse in the copyist's portions of the score only, while the autograph portion in this respect, too, goes far beyond the parts. We have indicated the trills and appoggiaturas taken from the parts by special signs: trills

by t and appoggiaturas by ≝ . Having in mind the presumably earlier dates of the parts, we considered the inclusion of these signs justified only if distinctively identified. [The distinction has been observed in this edition concerning appoggiaturas, but not concerning trills.—A. M.]

SPECIAL OBSERVATIONS AND ERRORS

The most significant passages are four in number:

(1) The scourging (No. 18).
(2) The tenor aria *Erwäge* (No. 32).
(3) The original uncertainty in the shape of the theme in the first 21 measures of the chorus *Lasset uns den nicht zerteilen* (No. 54).
(4) The unclear design of the bass in the same chorus, from measure 30 onwards.

The readings of these passages in the original material are both exceptional and unworthy of belief, and thorough revision seemed necessary. Such revision has been undertaken in only three instances, however, while the solution of the fourth remains an open question, and it has been reproduced exactly as it appears in the originals.

(1) The scourging, and (2) the tenor aria *Erwäge* (No. 32): In both numbers the questions concern faulty beaming (metric division) of the notes. Similar errors are so common [in the original materials of Bach's works] that as early as [BG] Volume VII, p. 21, they were characterized as stereotyped, and dealt with accordingly. But so remarkable a confusion as the present one (the Trautwein edition reproduces this confusion in part) could not be passed over without special mention. By comparing various passages it was possible to bring order into this aria. But for a recitative there is no such aid at hand. Subjective opinion has free play [in deciding about the composer's probable intentions]. We might have given the "scourging" in the version of some of the parts, in which the initial figure is carried through consistently. But a correction of Bach's in the original score, already mentioned, bade us give the latter the preference. [Query: What can "some of the parts" mean? Only one Evangelist's part is listed (cf. pp. 233 ff.); or do one or more of the continuo parts after all include the vocal line? The BG Foreword can only leave us wondering.—A. M.]

(3) The original uncertainty in the theme of the chorus *Lasset uns den nicht zerteilen*, No. 54. This uncertainty concerns the interval by which the final syllable of the word "losen", after the melisma, is approached. A comparison of the present edition with the Trautwein edition (pp. 80–81, m. 2) will show that the latter contains now major sevenths, now minor sevenths, now even repetitions of the same tone. In the original there are also ascending seconds and descending octaves. Apart from the fact that many of these leaps simply do not accord with the progressions in the other voices, so irregular a series of changes in the intervals in a theme must in itself seem strange. It becomes altogether incredible, however, when one sees that in the remainder of the piece the intervals mentioned do not occur at all, and instead the interval of a fifth is introduced and strictly carried through. This strict consistency extends over 34 measures, and we have applied it to the first 21 measures also, despite the fact that in measures 5 and 12 this results in octaves between the soprano and tenor. Concerning these octaves, we cannot be justifiably reproached. In both instances the soprano and tenor

already proceed in octaves, without the "altered note". The syncopated rhythm of the soprano does not affect this fact, as the following example shows:

Thus the fourth octave is only the inevitable continuation of the three preceding ones.

(4) The unclear design of the bass of the same chorus, from measure 30 onwards. This can be explained only by the assumption that in the earliest original (i.e., in the score made for the first version) some quarter-rests, and some of the stems added to the violoncello part to indicate the design of the bass line, were not wholly clear or were even missing.

All the surviving continuo parts, taken together with the (later) score, form a disorderly mass of contradictions.* The more accurate parts reveal, however, that the continuo is to play only the downward "passing tones", while in ascending it is to play only chord tones. For example, mm. 30-36:

For the harmonic purity of the complicated writing this design presents essential advantages.

DIVERGENCES IN DETAIL

No. 1, m. 82:  We consider this high d erroneous,

despite the fact that it is clear in the originals, since there is no obstacle to the alto's imitating the design in the bass two measures earlier. The design of the alto part taken separately also demands a lower tone, after the two preceding ascents to the high d, so that the high d immediately following may have its proper effect.

No. 11, m. 42: Continuo  But com-

pare mm. 4, 12, 24, etc.

No. 13: The obbligato instrument is not named in the original score. In the parts, however, the part is given to both flutes.

No. 14: At the end of the recitative, the following passage occurs in the original score:

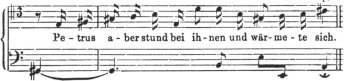

Pe - trus a - ber stund bei ih - nen und wär- me - te sich.

---

*This disorder is in turn evidence for the priority of the violoncello accompaniment. If in its stead a simple bass in quarter-notes had been notated, the divergent readings in the continuo parts would never have come about. This remark corrects one made in the Foreword to [BG] Volume V¹, p. 20. A clearer picture of the circumstances surrounding the various versions of this work was not possible previous to a complete study of the extensive (and hitherto not classified) original materials. —[BG footnote]

The parts show that this is the earlier reading of mm. 19-21. It is written so directly after the recitative, however, that at first glance one might imagine that it is the conclusion. The beginning of the copyist's work occurs, as has been stated, at m. 42, and it is the copyist who presented this passage in so distorted a manner. How the error arose is a question to which only speculative answers could be given. At the point where Bach's handwriting in the original score stops, the correctness of the score stops also. The copyist presents himself at once in so inaccurate a fashion that it is only from the tenor (Evangelist) part that one can tell how the second half of this 42nd measure should read.

No. 17, m. 8: In the parts, there are the following readings:

The original score has the third of these, and our edition follows it. The original idea and most natural of the readings is of course the first. The f♯ and the c♯ represent Bach's subsequent corrections of the octaves created with the tenor by the progression to the a.

No. 18: For the passage "*und weinete bitterlich*", the original score is again completely unusable.

No. 19: "*Tutti li Stromenti*" reads the caption in the original score, but nowhere else is there any indication of whether oboes and flutes were really intended to be included.

m. 44: In this aria, in the score, Bach had to correct his copyist's work in many places, especially in the viola. But in order not to make passages illegible by crossing them out, he found it necessary in many cases to resort to the expedient of writing in a different clef to make the already written notes stand for the correct ones. Thus in a variegated sequence we have not only the alto clef but also the violin clef, and at times the C-clef on the second line, already obsolete in Bach's own day. Nevertheless, Bach overlooked a considerable number of errors, notably in this measure, where the original

score reads:  . Following his example, we

have read the second, third, fourth, and fifth notes in the violin clef (transposed down an octave).

m. 69: In the original score, the continuo reads:

This makes a bad progression with the viola, so we have chosen the reading contained in the parts.

No. 23, mm. 14-15: The alto reads:  . Originally the

bass had the same reading, one beat earlier. It was changed, but Bach forgot the alto imitation of it.

No. 25, m. 14: The soprano reads:  , which is con-

tradicted by the following measure and by the opening of this number.

No. 26, m. 19: in the parts [part?], this reads:

We chose the reading in the score as superior.

No. 31: The original score is again very unreliable in this Arioso, so that the readings in the parts had to be followed, the more so since they contained the autograph interpolations described above. [Spitta stated that the text of this number, in both parts and score, was different from that given in BG. Schering, in the preface to his edition of the miniature score, gave a different reading still. I have chosen among these readings the details which fit the inflections of the music most closely, and which accordingly seem most likely to have been in Bach's mind when he composed it.—A. M.]

Nos. 34 and 50: Readings established by collation of the parts.

Nos. 38 and 42: Both choruses were full of errors, which, however, it has been possible to eliminate by collation of the materials. The parts helped toward clearing up these pieces, notably in mm. 28-29 of the alto of No. 38, which in the score

reads:  , and similarly in No. 42.

[BG, it seems to me, only partly straightened this passage out: perhaps the downward skip of a sixth, in place of the more natural fifth, between the fourth and fifth notes of m. 28 is only an error in BG.—A.M.]

No. 54, mm. 35-36: The alto reads:  , i.e.,

a instead of g. Cf. m. 22.

No. 63, m. 47: The soprano reads:  . But

compare m. 61, and elsewhere.

m. 99: The flute reads:  . But com-

pare m. 19, where the more correct reading, ab, occurs.

mm. 14, 56, and 125 are parallel. Since in the originals the latter two agree, it was to be assumed that the first contained an error, making the last 32nd in the flute a c, instead of the correct bb.

No. 67, m. 110: The viola reads: . But compare m. 46.

[The remaining remarks concern the numbers contained in the earlier versions of the St. John, subsequently dropped by Bach, and published in the appendix to BG XII¹.]